POSITION AT NOON

POSITION AT NOON

BY

ERIC LINKLATER

WITH DECORATIONS BY
HANS TISDALL

MACDONALD PUBLISHERS
Loanhead, Midlothian

Published by
Macdonald Publishers
Edgefield Road, Loanhead, Midlothian

ISBN 0 904265 38 2 hardback
0 904265 42 0 paperback

*The publishers acknowledge the financial
assistance of the Scottish Arts Council
in the publication of this volume*

Printed in Scotland by
Macdonald Printers (Edinburgh) Limited
Edgefield Road, Loanhead, Midlothian

Contents

TO
MY DEAR MU
WHO DEMANDED
A DEDICATION
I OFFER THIS
WITH LOVE

'For several days we had seen no sun, but now it shone with a sort of dissolute brilliance, and the Captain got his position at noon. He pricked the chart and gloomily declared that while it was some comfort to know where he was, he could find little satisfaction in counting how far he had come. To the north and east the sky was darkening, and the glass was falling.'

— *A Voyage to Port Musgrave.*

I The Darkest Hour

I WOKE with a three-dimensional hangover.

In bilious horror that filled a lurching, sea-sick world with the sound of muffled drums, I remembered in a dizzy acceptance of defeat the night before. I had drunk a bottle of rum and spent three hours on a haggard study of my accounts. They, as I expected, had pitilessly exposed my bankruptcy, and there was no comfort in realising that I had not been as deeply shocked by the discovery as I should have been. Emotionally as well as financially I was in the red, and beyond the reach of shock: or so I thought. I was in love with a slut of a girl who wore denim trousers over high-heeled shoes, smoked thirty or forty cigarettes a day, drank gin with an open throttle, and was indifferent to the state of her hair. I loved her with a passion hotly flavoured by bitter and useless recrimination.

On the credit side I had to admit that for a week or more my ulcer had given me no pain; but my recurrent back-sliding had found a new velocity. I had absolutely no faith in God — and for three days it had been raining.

Over the milky slop of her breakfast plate I saw my wife looking, not at me but in my direction, with an expression I knew too well. She was waiting to tell me something: waiting to catch my attention and turn on the tap. Both taps, it might be: warmly confidential, then cold for the grocer's bill. Or it might be something about the children: about the whimsical things they said, and then the rash on their bottoms and the new clothes they needed. I could see the pressure rising, but I gave her no chance. I read with a frowning absorption the morning's news, and found something less than comfort in it. The world was like a lethal quagmire towards which my bewildered country was blindly toboganning, and from the home front came only a recital of rising prices and falling output, a new Luddite rebellion, more juvenile delinquency, and a well-argued suicide. At that I smiled, with cynical approval, and looked up to tell her that we were now the poorer for the loss of a judicious mind. But she spoke first. She saw her opportunity, the warm tap gushed, and under it, like a drowning man, I listened to her lamentable secret.

I did not lose my temper — it pleases me to remember that — but I hurt her by a display of what she thought to be indifference; though it was, in fact, a very civil concealment of the dismay I felt. What was hardest to endure was the triumph in her voice as she told me she was pregnant again. It was not, I am sure, a vindictive triumph; but a lesser man might have thought it so. I said a word or two — nothing memorable, I fancy — and then she left me, her nose bright pink and dabbing at her eyes with a grubby handkerchief.

For another ten minutes I sat at the untidy table, too sick to move, too exhausted to think and add once more my varied debts. Idly I looked at the paper again, and saw that a horse I had meant to back — but forgotten, till it was too late — had come in at 33 to 1. And that, I thought, was the pattern of my life. The pattern and the habit — and presently habit took charge of me, and I went upstairs to dress.

I never used to shave and dress till after breakfast, for no one ever came to the shop before eleven; and there was still no hurry. But up I went, and in the conducive environment of our disgusting bath-room I remembered the suicide in the morning's news and contemplated the voluntary conclusion of my own life. I have always used the old-fashioned, open-bladed, cut-throat razor, and when my neck and chin were thickly fleeced with a snow-white flocculence of soap, I thought for a moment — with a shudder of absurd delight — of the startling beauty I could create by releasing, with a hard, decisive, bone-deep pull of the blade, a little waterfall of bright arterial blood to melt and wash away the lathered snow. To wash away, in a moment of beauty, the sordid accumulation of my insuperable difficulties and the utter confusion of my pointless existence.

But my eyes prevented me. I have very handsome eyes: large and luminous, dark brown under eloquent white lids. 'Speaking eyes' they have been called, and 'soulful'. Women have admired them excessively, and I myself can never see them in a mirror without, at the least, a modest gratification, and in better moods an answering pride. The mirror, it is true, reflected more than a pair of loquacious bright irises, enigmatically gleaming pupils, and eyelids a little weary but undefeated. It showed a segment of grimily tattered wall-paper, some part of the desquamating rim of a rusty-bottomed bath, and the broken seat of a stool that was never quite clean. I shrugged my shoulders and looked through the little window at the rain, falling with sullen persistence on the cobbled street, and at the house opposite; where Edna lived and worked.

My shop, and undesirable residence, were on a corner of the High Street. Over the principal window was the lettering in tarnished gold: A. C. BIRTWHISTLE, *Antiques*. That window displayed, and had done for a month past, a grand-father clock with a brass face, a pseudo-Chippendale side-board and a couple of re-built Chippendale chairs, a gate-legged table, and the two pale horses which, on a day of catastrophic self-confidence, I had thought were T'ang. Above the lesser window, that looked on Church Street, was a declaration in smaller script of *Porcelain, Old Silver, Books and Curios*. And facing that window, on the other corner, stood THE BUTTERMERE FAMILY HOTEL, *Open to Non-Residents, Licensed*, etc., *Proprietrix, Mrs. M. O. BUTTER-MERE*. Edna's mother.

Edna was twenty-two, and dressed-up for evening service behind the bar — saloon bar only, a small but steady trade — she was a winsome, lovely creature. But in the morning, my God, what a trollop! She and the Austrian girl who worked there would come out to shake mats, take in the milk, buy something or other at the chemist's on the other side of the street, and stand talking with anyone they knew — looking like trollops! Faded blue denim trousers, shabbily and tightly covering the bounce of their tautly exuberant be-hinds, and their ankles insecure over tottering shoes; their heads tied up in dusters, and cigarettes hanging from lips newly painted though their cheeks were still greasy with sleep; torn jerseys or loosely buttoned blouses and a posture like black women at the doors of a sun-bleached shanty-town. But they worked hard, I admit that. Mrs. Butter-mere, the Austrian girl, Edna and her sister Lily and an old, decrepit, varicose-veined waiter were the whole staff of the Buttermere Family Hotel, and for half the year their dozen-or-so bedrooms were always full, and eight or ten local business-men had lunch there every day. But in this country people will eat anything nowadays.

It was Lily who first attracted me. Lily, three years older than Edna, had superior tastes — or pretended to them — and a remarkable figure too. The four women, indeed (Mrs Buttermere, at forty-eight, the biggest of them all), were re-markable for the development and uninhibited display of their feminine quality; and Lily, to her bosom, added an interest in English literature. She bought from me (it was in poor condition and she got it cheap) a copy of the Nonesuch edition of the Love Poems of John Donne, and turning over its pages, as if in doubt of the price I should ask, I carelessly drew her attention to the lines:

> 'I can love her, and her, and you, and you;
> I can love any, so she be not true.'

But Lily said scornfully, 'That's a young man boasting, hoping to shock his friends,' and I realised a different approach was necessary; if indeed she was approachable by any route.

But she came back a week later and bought a red wine-glass (ten shillings) which may or may not have been Venetian; and two nights later I took her to the cinema to see an Italian film that should have opened her mind — if her mind was that sort — to some idea of passion. To some interest in it, I had hoped. But not a bit of it. She talked about directors, lighting, camera angles and so forth. Then about literature, and affected familiarity with it in the way of people who affect understanding and friendship with a visiting celebrity to whom they have said 'How d'you do' at a public dinner. But she wouldn't suffer any familiarity from me. She brushed me off and went back to literature. It meant so much to her, she said.

But one wasted evening wasn't enough to discourage me, and I wasted three or four more. She would have enjoyed a long siege — that I discovered — but long sieges aren't to my liking, and one night I went over to the hotel with the intention of telling her so. I meant to speak plainly and get a plain answer; pretending I didn't know what the answer would be.

Edna was alone in the bar — it was near closing-time —

and Lily, she told me, had gone to a meeting of the Melbury Amateur Dramatic Club. She was on the committee, said Edna, who was very surprised to learn that I wasn't on it too. 'I thought that was where your common interest lay,' she said. 'Culture, and that sort of thing. Lily isn't sexy, is she? Though you might think so from her appearance.'

She looked at me appraisingly, as a fisherman considers the possibilities of some unfamiliar stretch of water; and with a sudden awareness that I too was on the bank of a new river, I offered her a drink.

'Well, thanks,' she said, 'I'll take a gin and french.'

'Make it a big one,' I said.

'Saves time, doesn't it?' she answered, and having been generous with the gin, was parsimonious with Noilly Prat. 'Cheers,' she said.

I had first seen her — or perhaps I should say I had first noticed her existence — in her morning costume, and though I had recognised her careless good looks and the *bravura* of her figure, I had disliked her sluttish costume and the absence of taste that let her walk in public in trousers and high-heeled, down-at-heel shoes. I labelled her a sloven, and thought no more of her. I saw her occasionally behind her sedately managed bar, and with casual interest remarked her improved appearance; but I rarely went there, and my morning image of her still prevailed. During my first five or six years in the town I had plenty to think of without bothering about my neighbours in the Buttermere Family Hotel.

But now I looked at her with a stirring of excitement. Lily was the handsomer of the two, but Edna had a moist eye, a more generous mouth, and her breasts were comely and hospitable, not assertive as Lily's were: who, for some inscrutable purpose of her own, hoisted them to an aggressive level. And Edna drank her gin and french with engaging appetite, with no genteel pretence to moderation of enjoyment.

14

'How you manage to live and work in that fusty, dusty shop full of worm-eaten furniture, and oil paintings of stags and roses, and china dogs, and books no human being would ever want to read — well, I just can't imagine,' she said. 'A man like you!' she added.

'It's possible,' I said, 'that I shan't be living there much longer.'

'Well,' she said, 'we're all of us better for a change, now and then.'

That was six or seven months ago, when I was already aware that my career as a dealer in antique furniture, porcelain and old silver was painfully approaching its natural end. And fatally, that evening, I found a lenitive for my increasing sensation of despair. I was given, as it were on a platter, a double helping of nirvana to medicine me against catastrophe. I discovered an agency of ineffable delight that isolated me all through a fine summer from any urgent thought or care for the inevitable winter of calamity. I bought Edna another drink, she gave me a large brandy and soda, and about eleven o'clock we went to look at the Abbey by moonlight. The Abbey grounds are extensive and well shaded, but the local inhabitants make little use of them for fear of ghosts; the local amorists prefer the municipal park or the banks of the river. We had, then, no fear of interruption, and beneath the mulberry tree whose age the guide-books so piously exaggerate we invaded and made conquest of the improbable domain of bliss.

It was, however, a domain that I shall not chart; for I was brought up to observe a decent reticence. I was, indeed, very well brought up. Till 1939 my father and mother kept a cook, three maids, a gardener and a gardener's boy. That was the standard of respectability under which I grew to manhood, and I am pleased to think that I still recognise certain rules of behaviour which were then taught me. I

have, therefore, no intention of describing the physical trans-
ports that made so memorable — oh, unique! — my illicit,
tumble-down, furtively recurrent but cosmically satisfying
union with Edna. But because of it I had, in my squalid
bath-room, a burning, gloomy, exhausted glory of knowledge
that put me (I do not flatter myself) among those who had
ridden legendary tournaments in the lists of love.

I thought of François Villon and his binding, abominable
attachment to Fat Margot of the *bordeau ou tenons nostre estat.* I
remembered Des Grieux' obsessive love of Manon Lescaut.
I recalled that fabulous adventure of a young officer of the
Indian Army — or, more plausibly, a young official of the
old East India Company — who had the superlative good
fortune to meet in love a temple prostitute in Madura,
Trichinopoli, Seringapatam or some such holy place in
southern India: that exquisite, god-bound, god-intoxicated
girl had been so perfectly taught the arts of love which uni-
fied her with her god that the young Englishman experienced
such a joy as none of his fellow-countrymen had ever
imagined — much less known — but after separation from
his sublime, inspired, and supernacular tart (or *devadasi*) he
fell into irreparable melancholy from the certainty that
never again would he know an even faintly comparable
happiness. That melancholy was also mine; for within the
next day or two — I told myself — the Buttermere Family
Hotel and my *devadasi* would be as far from me as Madura
or Trichinopoli.

Yes, Edna to me was Fat Margot, Manon, and the fabled
prostitute. To me, a bankrupt dealer in spurious antiques,
she was the intoxication of opium, hashish, and mescalin all
together. She was the word of bliss made flesh — flesh melting into bliss — and under the mulberry tree, under other
trees, in the secrecy of her own bed occasionally, and in
rattle-springed, thin-mattressed beds in nearby cheap hotels

I forfeited my wits and threw away my last chance of rescuing some little raft of solvency from the imminence of total shipwreck. For Edna was expensive, bless her heart — and bless too her other portions of dear excellence.

None of us, however, stands alone. We, and the events we motivate, are all part and parcel of one another and of farther events. My wife's untimely pregnancy was wholly due to my infatuation with Edna, which, because I could not conceal it, woke in her a furibund jealousy that none of my previous little errands in emotion (being manageable and discreetly managed) had ever aroused. Within the narrowest definition of sex my wife was not unduly exigent, but she had, as a wife, a lively sense of what was her due; and I, having sworn that my interest in Edna was no more than a playful sentiment, felt obliged by mere decency to assure a still unhappy woman of my truly marital affection. Of which, I feel, she took grossly unfair advantage.

I first met my wife soon after my mother's death, when it became necessary to sell the small property I had inherited. In my youth, as I have said, my father and my mother kept a very good house, and were properly attended — and from this lost anchorage I must, I think, make a little voyage and say something of my early life. I shall not, however, be tedious.

In 1937 I went from my public school — not one of the best — to the University of Cambridge, and chose to read History; as did many other young men in whom there was no commanding impulse to carve a great career for themselves out of the hardness of the world, but who felt that the world still offered a comfortable living to anyone whose antecedents showed he was used to comfort and would not abuse it. This reasonable expectation was defeated by the outbreak of war, and many who had made no provision for disaster suffered deeply. I myself endured much, but less than others because I had done what I could to insure myself against the hazards of our time by joining the volunteer reserve of the Royal Air Force. — Not, of course, as a flying officer. My semi-circular canals prevented that. The semi-circular canals, I am told, are an essential part of the inner ear, and no one can be a pilot whose canals are not in tip-top shape. But mine, it seemed, had crumbling banks, were over-grown with weed, had leaking locks or some such thing — in short, I could not fly without feeling giddier than an Edwardian governess on a swing. That fortunate disability kept me on the ground, and gave me an office job that filled my next six years.

England, West Africa, and Ceylon: that was the scope or ambit of my service, and after leaving England I was never in grave danger from enemy action. But I had, of course, to endure much discomfort and long seasons of enervating boredom. I could not, I think, have suffered, without loss of my sanity, the boredom of war had I not taken a constant interest in its economy: which was deplorably ungoverned. The waste was shocking, and all I could save — of stores that were likely to become superfluous, and would be left to rust, or of commodities whose scarcity gave them a grossly in-flated value — was no more than a pint or two from an ocean of squandering. But it did give me a bank account of two or three thousand pounds, and except for that, my war service was unrewarded. I was demobilised in March, 1946, with the rank of Squadron-Leader, and all the Government gave me was a paltry gratuity of £130 and a few medals that were so cheaply and coarsely made I am now almost ashamed to wear them. This, I am sure, was the deliberate intention of the Labour Party, then in power.

I did not demand immediate employment, after putting off my uniform, but it would be wrong to say that I was idle for the next year or two. I was, on the contrary, keenly aware of the passing scene and always on the look-out for an opportunity in which to invest — with some hope of profit — my talents and the remnant of my savings. But nothing came my way, and from time to time I spent some months at home. Fortunately I was on good terms with my mother, but my father, who had served in a war that killed all his contemporaries, regarded my continued existence as a proof either of God's injustice or my skrimshanking. He was embittered, of course, by the diminishment of his estate and the loss of the servants on whom he had depended for his comfort. In 1948, when he died, he was not an old man — he was only fifty-nine — but he looked old and felt old; and because he had failed to make proper arrangements his remnant estate was badly cut up by death duty. My mother tried to recoup her losses by rash investment, and when she was killed in a motor-car accident two years later my inheritance had dwindled to three or four thousand pounds and the dust-sheeted contents of the echoing, servantless house in a corner of which she had been living without comfort, or, I must admit, complaint.

I adored my mother, but I could not sympathise — until after her death — with her hobby of collecting Staffordshire pottery. She had over two hundred of those absurd, ungainly, crudely coloured figures of sailors, cricketers, cats and cockerels — Toby jugs of all sorts, Albanian bandits and dogs by the dozen — milkmaids and monarchs — a vast parade of heavy-handed whimsy for which I could see no excuse at all until Olive Trumbull, who became my wife, told me what they were worth in hard cash.

'There's enough in this house to stock an antique shop,' she said. 'Pity old Birtwhistle's on his last legs. Ten years ago he'd have bought everything at sight, and saved you a lot of trouble.'

Olive was the eldest daughter of George Trumbull, senior, and sister of George T., junior, of Trumbull, Tranter and

Payne, Auctioneers, Valuators, and Estate Agents: a very prosperous firm indeed, much esteemed and influential in Melbury. Her father had come to inspect the house and its contents, to advise me about their disposal; and she had come with him to gratify a natural curiosity. She did that, and dropped an idea into my mind that took root and quickly grew. Here, it seemed, was the answer to a question I could no longer ignore. How (to be brief) was I to earn my living? I had made trial of several ways or by-ways to a competence, and found myself temperamentally unsuited to copy-writing for an advertising firm; to selling motor-cars in Great Portland Street; and to travelling (in a commercial way) on behalf of varnish, foundation garments, and ecclesiastical furniture. But now, it appeared, I could become — and that with a minimum of trouble — a dealer in antiques.

In Olive's opinion — who seemed shrewd and knowledgeable — I had enough to stock my shop, and I had heard that old Birtwhistle could not live much longer. I had known him from boyhood, for we lived only a couple of miles out of Melbury, and in his prime his shop had been, to my youthful vision, a very gold-mine of fascination. I remembered a tiger-skin with a snarling head; a sailing-ship under a glass dome; a set of fantastically carved Indian chess-men; a cabinet of butterflies; and a tall bronze figure of a shinily naked girl. What a pleasure it would be to deal in such things! And, of course, having been brought up among good furniture and with Georgian silver on the table, I knew enough to tell the difference between good and bad, between the genuine and the spurious. When, having sold my original stock for a handsome price, I set out to buy more, I was not likely to be deceived. Or so I thought.

The upshot was that I bought old Birtwhistle's premises when he died, and decided to carry on business under his name; which was widely known in the district. And I married Olive. She was quite good-looking in a restrained, unobstrusive way, and well educated: Cheltenham Ladies' College, in fact. She had a little money of her own, and would presumably come into more when her father died; and in the meantime a connexion with Trumbull, Tranter and Payne could hardly fail to help me in my new way of life. For a year or two it was, indeed, very useful; but then I fell out with George T., junior, who had the astonishing ill manners to interfere (or try to) in my private life.

'Remember,' he said — at ten o'clock in the morning, in his office, to which I had received an urgent summons — 'remember you are married to my sister! And if your memory does fail you, I have something here that'll re-inforce it!'

From the floor beside his chair he picked up a hunting-crop — I could hardly believe my eyes — and smacked the top of his desk with it. A ludicrous display! So ludicrous that, fortunately for him, I was not really offended. And, of course, he was only bluffing. He was as white as his own blotting-paper, and his voice so tremulous he could hardly speak. I excused his behaviour, but our friendship did not survive so vulgar a display of temper.

Olive, poor girl, had been talking too much. She had let her family know that our union was not as happy as we had all hoped it would be; and though I didn't blame her for her indiscretion, I regretted it. I was hurt by it. It made life less pleasant for both of us. And though she bore me two children within twenty-four months of our marriage — which should, I think, have contented any reasonable woman — she persisted in complaining that I neglected her.

The difficulties arising from incompatibility, and from her garrulous habit, were aggravated by the disappoint-ingly small profits of the shop. Most of my inherited furni-ture sold well enough — some of it very well — and my mother's collection of two hundred and twenty pieces of Staffordshire pottery went, as they say, like hot cakes; but after the last revolting Toby jug had gone, I encountered a lot of disappointment. No one would buy my father's house, which was too big for the post-war habit of life and affected by dry rot so apparent that denial of it was useless; and repeatedly I was swindled by charming, innocent-seeming, dignified old ladies who sold me Sheraton chairs, ormolu cabinets, Empire sofas, and Limerick glass that had been, so they solemnly assured me, in their families for many generations, but which, on closer inspection, turned out to be the work of unscrupulous fabricators of our own times. It was from an old lady with the manners of a duchess, the candour of a child, and the probity (as it seemed) of a Scotch Presbyterian that I bought the two pale horses that I thought, and she swore, were genuine T'ang.

But I promised not to be tedious, and because a story of disappointment, decay, and the approach of destitution is all too likely to be tedious, I shall say no more of the collapse of my business and the dissolution of my hopes. On that morning of bilious admission I stood face to face with bankruptcy — and through the grimy window of my squalid little bath-room, beyond the rain in the street, was the Buttermere Family Hotel, whose shining wet roof sheltered my *devadasi*, my Manon, the unutterable beatitudes of my sluttish queen.

The pockets of my dressing-gown were full of cheap, buff-coloured envelopes that I would not open because I could not pay the bills they held; and I had begun to tear them up, to throw them in the discoloured water-bowl, when some uneasiness of my mind took me to the window again — and there, across the street, at the side-door of the hotel, Edna, at that moment, exhibited herself in her faded blue denim trousers, a woollen body-garment of horrible shape and nigger-pink in colour, with a duster so tied about her head that its knots stood up like a rabbit's ears. She had a cigarette between her lips, she looked at the rain, shuddered, and went in again....

I had been lost in thought, captured by the panorama of time past, and the soap on my cheeks had dried to a thin crust. For a fleeting instant the thought of suicide returned, but again my eyes rebuked the thought. I lathered my face anew, and shaved with slow, deliberate care.

My complexion was too dark — discoloured by a liverish tendency, perhaps — but even in comparison with the magnificence of my eyes, my features were good enough. In youth, I had sometimes thought of the Church as a vocation, for religion has always been, if not a persistent, at least one of my recurrent interests; and certainly I should wear with dignity a bishop's mitre and dalmatic, and look very well in them. But I could never feel sure that preferment would come my way, and rather than live out my life as a parish priest, I put aside episcopal ambition and resigned myself to secular interests.

Perhaps I have created a false impression — an impression of vanity — by admitting the pleasure and satisfaction my looking-glass gives me; but it would be dishonest to deny its effect, and *suppressio veri* to say nothing about it. I do, in fact, consider my appearance quite objectively, and in lighter mood I have often admitted that my natural solemnity of expression, and the heavy cast of my features, would suit a butler as well as a bishop — the old-fashioned, magisterial sort of butler, that is — and in my business, indeed, when questioned about the provenance of a commode or a piece of silver, I have sometimes pretended that it came into my possession in consequence of long service to My Lord So-and-So or the Earl of Such-and-Such.

It is curious to think that my name also would equally

grace a cathedral close or ennoble a pantry. Edward Gratiano Vanbrugh: so by baptism and descent was I endowed, and no one will deny the propriety of praying for 'Gratiano our Bishop' — I would, in those circumstances, have discarded Edward — or of signing an episcopal letter *Gratiano Sarum, Gratiano Bath: et Well:*, or *Gratiano Winton:*.

Take, then, the other alternative — and how impossible to doubt the gratification of any employer, even the noblest, in calling 'Vanbrugh!' to summon his butler! It is a noble name, sonorous and resounding. It would echo proudly in a baron's hall, and in some lesser, modern house evoke the grandeur of a vanished yet unforgotten past. But in this shrunken world how many employers are there who could afford a butler named Vanbrugh? There was no more substance in that hope than in my dreams of the episcopate.

I dressed carefully, as I always do. I never yielded to the temptation to wear artistic or Bohemian clothes because I had become an antique dealer, but merely allowed myself to enliven with a little colour what a gentleman would naturally wear in the country. That morning, I remember, I put on a rather old but very well cut fine tweed suit, a maroon waistcoat with brass buttons, and a tie of yellow flannel. I went down to the shop, and in a darkly spotted cheval glass considered my reflexion with quiet approval.

But there was little else in my surroundings of which I could approve. A complete set of Ruskin in green leather binding, a mahogany wardrobe built (as it seemed) for a Victorian family of fourteen, and a six-foot-long stuffed alligator were among the nearer exhibits. There was some Benares brass, and a few pieces of Sheffield plate that looked almost as yellow. There were two side-tables described as 'in the style of Robert Adam', a set (with many volumes missing) of the *Annual Register* from 1759, and a Chinese cabinet that had once been prettily inlaid with mother-ofpearl. There was a barometer of commanding size, and a globe of the world with a dark red stain obscuring North America. There was a noble mirror surmounted by a gilded eagle whose wings I had stuck on with Seccotine....

My inspection of these lamentable objects was interrupted by Olive, who came to say she was taking the children out for a walk, and would not be home for lunch. She was going to have lunch with her mother.

'And she, I hope, will be more interested in what I have to tell her than you were,' she said. 'Anyway, you'll have to look after yourself till tea-time.'

It is a sad confession, but I have to admit that I felt no great affection for my two children, and the prospect of a third quite appalled me. It is widely accepted, I know, that a man not merely ought to, but in the nature of things must, love his offspring. This opinion, however, ignores the all-too-obvious fact that many children are really not lovable. No one would hesitate to describe an adult acquaintance as a dull, snivelling, pasty-faced, and egocentric bore — but how many pause in the moment of criticism to remember that the adult was once young, and in all probability as unattractive in childhood as in maturity? And why, if we are clear-sighted about our grown-up friends, should we be myopic in the nursery?

I watched them pass the window — my wife and her pigeon-pair — and with the stoicism of which I am capable at such a moment, I spoke aloud the superb defiance of Parolles: 'Simply the thing I am shall make me live!'

In a certain mood Parolles is my favourite character in all literature. When the skies fall and light is blotted out, then I think of him: discountenanced, stript of pretence, naked to shame, and with stark honesty admitting his little-ness and recognising its advantage — 'If my heart were great 'twould burst at this,' he says — but because of honesty and some undying germ of life, he is undefeated, undismayed. When things go wrong, Parolles is my man.

When things go right I believe in God, of course, and have nobler heroes. When I was a boy I had great aspirations to virtue, and spent much of my time in company with its splendid myths: from Britomart and King Arthur to Alan Quatermain and Sir Nigel Loring, from *Deeds That Won the Empire* and *Fights for the Flag* to Newbolt and — now who was the other fellow? There were several others, but of late years I haven't cultivated them much, and their names have slipped my memory. Of late years I have felt closer to Parolles.

Under a certain sort of judgment this, I suppose, admits a descent from the *piano nobile* to the servants' hall; but I could not blame myself for the decline. Circumstances had been adverse — there was no doubt of that — and behind the circumstances loomed the figure of my father. I hesitated to blame a man who was no longer there to defend himself, but my father could not be absolved.

For the unhappiness of that morning, as well as for the diminishment of my ideals, my father, at the final judgment, must accept responsibility. He, not I, was culpable. Or — to put it generously — more culpable than I.

II Tragedy and Farce

IN 1914 my father was one of the fine flowers of England's youth, a shapely blossom on a sturdy bough of its strong history. By 1939 he was an elderly, unhappy man, devoid of will and deprived of hope, who would say, when he saw the usual crowd of people in the High Street on a Saturday night, or a throng of young men pushing forward to watch a football match, 'Do you think we could have held the Salient with those chaps? Don't you believe it!'

In 1914 he was an athlete, a cricketer, something of a scholar and handsomer than a magazine-artist's drawing of a young hero. Handsomer because, in addition to an orthodox square chin, broad brow, bold cheekbones, he had eyes that expressed a charming and wide-open faith. — But if you ask me faith in what, I must admit I do not know: or do not fully know. Faith in England — yes. Faith in the progress and growth of human intelligence, human charity — almost certainly. Faith in bettering the world by an application of scientific knowledge, an English sense of responsibility, and the shining decency of conduct taught in English schools — beyond a doubt. Faith in God — well, it depends on what you mean by God.

In a journal that he kept for most of his life — but

intermittently, and with ever longer intermissions — there is an entry, in March, 1914, that reads:

It is necessary, though often difficult, to live in a mannerly, unobtrusive humility: a humility of the spirit, *bien entendu*.

It is of the utmost value, and very easy, thank God, to believe in both the beauty and the salutary effect of laughter.

It is, above all, essential to see and trust the individual worth, importance, and excellence of one's friends — and to admit, by implication, that other people's friends may have a comparable importance.

So much I realise, and accept. But when, unthinkingly and instinctively, I write 'thank God' — as I have done — what do I mean by 'God'? And this question I cannot answer. That I believe in 'Something' it would be absurd to doubt when my instinct is spontaneous gratitude to It; but in my mind, of course, there is nothing that even distantly resembles the old gentleman with a long beard and stern, judicial eyes who haunted every properly taught Victorian nursery. There is, however, something much more definite than Creative Evolution, and I must admit a comforting belief that my faith, and the faith of my friends, in the goodness of humility, laughter, and the individual is in accordance with Its view of life: that It — dare I say so? — has an English complexion, if not an English constitution.

That is very prettily said. I like it — more than a Frenchman or a New Yorker would — and I wish my youth had been as happy as my father's. His happiness — and this goes far beyond our comprehension — even survived the declaration of war. His happiness, and the happiness of nearly all his generation, were indeed enhanced by war; for when Rupert Brooke wrote, 'Now God be thanked Who has matched us with His hour,' he wrote not only for my father and every one of his friends, but for a whole multitude of men of every class, creed, and condition.

Quite, quite incomprehensible to us; but none the less true. In 1914, of course, the English were bedevilled by all manner of things that we have forgotten: boredom with their own comfort, fear of civil war in Ireland, a deep uneasiness about social conditions, and a superstitious dread of the women's revolt. Those Suffragettes really frightened them, and to go to war with Uhlans and the Prussian Guard was probably a real, if temporary relief from worrying about Mrs Pankhurst and her companions.

But there was more to it than that. There was a deep and genuine feeling that good had separated itself from evil: that good and evil now stood on opposite sides, and our young men had the chance of a lifetime to enlist under their own colours. Which they did. They enlisted to fight for small nations, to win a war that would put an end to war — and for week after week in the pouring rain, for month after wintry month in ramshackle barracks and overcrowded billets, they lived in faith unsoiled, with enthusiasm undiminished, and drilled with wooden guns and wore under the winter rain their own civvy suits till they rotted on their shoulders because the England of their hearts could neither clothe them in the King's uniform nor give them the rifles for which they yearned.

England in the winter of 1914 stood in a spirit almost as remote from ours as the England of Francis Drake or Nelson's captains — and my poor, disconsolate, bleating father was, in his day, one of a hundred thousand golden lads whose radiance repelled the drenching skies, and kept their shabby billets warm, and lifted their hearts in wild, hilarious song as interminably they marched, and marched again, through the dripping, sodden, December lanes of England.

My poor father! My most fortunate and ludicrously defeated father! He had his bright morning, but there was thunder before noon, and in the evening of his life he walked, not knowing where, under drooping skies. His life was tragical, for in his youth he played a hero's part, with a fine deluding motive for his heroism, and the slow years of his dying went to a tune of dull bewilderment and witless complaint. And yet — I say this reluctantly, but it must be said — his tragedy cannot be taken as seriously as it deserves because the very core of it was low comedy: farcical comedy that jumped into his story like a clown through a paper hoop.

Perhaps he made too much of the need for humility; perhaps, behind a front of confidence and gay security, he felt some insufficiency of character or temper. Whatever the reason, when war came he refused a commission and in mid-August enlisted in the ranks of a Fusilier battalion. He was one of the First Hundred Thousand.

His battalion was sent to Aldershot, and late in October he and his fellow volunteers were at last given a makeshift uniform known as 'Kitchener blues'. Just in time, for most of them were in a scarecrow state by then. For the first week the Army had not even been able to give them knives, forks, and spoons. They had eaten with their fingers, prying salmon from a tin and washing out the tin to make in turn a tea-cup, a shaving-mug, and a bowl for greasy stew; they had slept on the ground, or a wooden floor, with a single blanket over them. But father never complained. Here is a page from his journal dated 28 October 1914:

Patience: that is essential. Patience and understanding. England was unprepared for a continental war, and that is why we have to put up with absurd discomfort, revolting food, quarters that no good farmer would keep his cattle in, and the mortification of going on parade without any of the weapons we should be learning to use. I can't in honesty blame the Government, for I myself was quite as short-sighted as Mr Asquith and his Cabinet: I am fully as intelligent as most of them, and no more than they did I expect war. But life is very unpleasant, and would be intolerable if it weren't for the feeling that, historically, we are doing not only a right and necessary thing, but something of immeasurable value for the future.

We are a very mixed lot. Some perfectly splendid people, and others — well, decidedly rough and disagreeable. Nearly all use monotonously appalling language, and at night the stench in the overcrowded barrack-room is quite sickening. In the last week we have had six desertions from my company, and fortunately the deserters were all men we were glad to be rid of. They and many others joined the Army not for principle or patriotic reason, but because they were out of work and hungry — or wanted to escape from wives even more unpleasant than themselves — or thought the Army meant endless beer and an easy life. They were very disappointed when they found that our nominal pay of one shilling and twopence a day sometimes came to no more than six shillings a week because of 'stoppages' for boot-polish, button-polish, barrack-damages and so forth. I am very lucky in comparison with the majority, for a few shillings don't matter to me — but how I wish it would stop raining!

We look perfect fools in our so-called 'Kitchener' uniform, and those of us who want to cut a dash with the girls feel very aggrieved. But in old folk-tales the hero was usually bewildered, befuddled and befooled for a start, and won his prize by endurance of humiliation. And so, I daresay, it will happen with us. I am on coal-fatigue to-morrow....

There is a taste of my father in his most critical mood; and I shall not quote him in a lyrical temper. I grow embarrassed and dispirited when I read his descriptions of route-marching, for example. They did an immense amount of marching — because, I suppose, their officers could think of nothing else to do — and my extraordinary father enjoyed it. They sang as they marched, and he records their ridiculous songs. There was one that went:

'Oh, I do like to be beside the sea-side,
  I do like to be beside the sea,
I do like to stroll along the prom-prom-prom,
  Where the brass bands play Tiddle-om-pom-pom....'

And another that archly enquired:

'Who were you with last night,
  Out in the pale moonlight?'

Then, excusing inanity with the solemn remark that 'This appears to be genuine folk-song in a modern idiom,' he writes down a nonsensical jingle that in 1915, he says, became very popular:

'When the moon shines bright on Charlie Chaplin,
  His boots are crackin',
  For want of blackin',
And his little baggy trousers they need mending,
  Before we send 'im
  To the Dardanelles!'

Also, to my surprise, he leaves a full copy of a very bawdy song that begins, 'There was a Jolly Tinker'.

'How my heart expands when I find myself one of a

chorus, eight or nine hundred strong, bellowing with the greatest good-will these simple, foolish ditties,' he writes. 'In that community of feeling and of purpose I know, for a certainty, that in even the nastiest of my companions there is something good; and I am glad to be one of them, not for their scrap of goodness, but for themselves.' He also says that he has grown quite fond of digging, and gravely adds: 'This is very fortunate because, now that spades have been issued, we practise digging trenches two days a week; and then, of course, we have to fill them in again.'

I shall not be so ingenuous as to say of him, 'How ingenuous!' These little extracts speak for themselves, and show quite clearly the fantastic difference between my father and myself. Between him, indeed, and all — or nearly all — of my generation. My silly father! How he was disillusioned.

He went to France in 1915, and received his baptism of fire at Loos; where his battalion, part of a reserve that had been kept sixteen miles behind the opening battle, had suddenly to march through a chaos of unordered traffic and then — weary, disorganised, and inexperienced — attack a German defence that had recovered from our first assault, and was well prepared for the next. The battalion, in three days' fighting, lost 19 officers and 480 other ranks. My father, by then a sergeant, was commissioned on the field, and in his journal wrote:

Never in my life have I known so profound a sense of tragedy, so agonising a pity, with a bewildering sense of glory — mingled, I must admit, with a great relief to be still alive — that transcends all other emotion. Mr Stanton, poor little Perkins, dear Sergeant Bullen — these and twenty others whom I knew and loved are dead, or mutilated beyond recovery, and hundreds of others. I think our battle was badly planned, and I know that the German machine-gun fire was such as no human beings could face and survive. But we did face it, and some of us are still drawing our rations. A man alive — well drilled and disciplined, purposive and forgetful of himself — is the most magnificent thing in God's creation; and a dead man, blown to shreds and gobbets by a shell, the most nauseating. Already I begin to feel alone in the world. I have been given a commission — and what I am committed to is war, that will kill all I love except honour.

Honour, good God! What does he mean by it? A tomfool, sentimental loyalty to a regiment he had never heard of a couple of years before? Or a wildly inflated notion of his own importance — his own necessity to live up to his romantic notion of what an Englishman should be, whose Englishness depended on England's successful exploitation of India, Africa, and the blackness of its own coalfields and industrial towns? 'Honour', without a solid foundation of common sense, seems to me such thistledown nonsense as a village idiot would blow away.

And, of course, that war — the Kaiser's war, the war of 1914 — was fought without any common sense. A vast field army, the biggest we had ever mustered, was condemned for nearly four years to attack an impregnable fortress; and that is the very pit and bottom of military science, if such a thing exists. — To besiege a fortress, that's reasonable; but to belabour the unshakable walls of a fortress with an army of marching men is merely to ruin the marching army — and that's what we did, and my father recognised it. Again and again he deplores the inhuman sacrifice of newly trained, full-fed, and beautifully drilled battalions thrown in impossible attack against the guns, mortars, pill-boxes, curtains

34

of wire, and encircling moat of mud of the German position; but never does he condemn it. He himself survived it all, and grew ever more sad of heart, more puzzled in his simple mind.

Ypres and the Somme, Arras and Vimy Ridge, Plugstreet, Bapaume — all those names reeking of mud, blood, and disaster recur in his journal. The Menin Gate and Passchendaele, Kemmel and St Eloi and Beaumont Hamel. Sanctuary Wood....

Somewhere he writes:

The battalion, 900 strong to begin with, was reformed as a single company.... What sort of physiological change is it that turns the ruddy, sunburnt cheeks of a well-fed youngster of nineteen or twenty to the grey of an old sand-bag after two or three days of battle.... So difficult to dig when the ground has been fought over before, and the clay is lumpy with old corpses. The French are very careless in disposing of their dead.... Carrying water (through a water-logged landscape) to our forward positions at Passchendaele, I met a boy of eighteen, one of our last draft, crying under the burden of his load. He was carrying two petrol tins, full of water, and here and there the mud came over his boot-tops where the duck-boards we had laid had been shot to pieces. He had some excuse, because his hands were frozen, but he was a silly boy. He should have found an old rifle-sling and taken the weight of his load on his shoulders. ... After that it froze in earnest, and we suffered a lot from frost-bite. But the battalion that relieved us were worse hit, for in a sudden thaw, when the whole of that frightful Passchendaele area seemed to melt beneath us, they lost twenty-seven drowned as they came out.... I am drinking rather more than I used to. I don't get drunk, as some poor chaps do, but before the last attack I drank a mug of neat whisky and felt much the better for it. Afterwards, when taking roll-call and counting the miserable remnant of my company, I needed half a bottle. But I wrote letters to 36 wives and mothers....

He was wounded two or three times, but not seriously except in the summer of 1917, when he was sent to a hospital in Hereford, where he met my mother: the girl, that is, who became my mother. She was a nurse, of course: a volunteer of the sort they called V.A.D. — and how I envy him his good luck! For my mother was adorable.

I have innumerable photographs of her: family snap-shots for the most part. She came of a family that, in a social way, was much the same as my father's; but more amiable. They seem to have spent a lot of their time going for picnics, bathing-parties, tennis-parties — and photographing each other. In nearly every group my mother is the belle and the prize and the laughing centre. Pretty as dog-roses in a sun-shot April shower — laughing like a school-girl at a circus clown — graceful as a ballet-dancer despite long skirts and a straw boater — then serious and dedicated in her clumsy V.A.D. uniform.

She was posted to the little hospital where father was convalescing just three days before he returned to his reserve battalion, but in that short time he fell deeply and solemnly in love with her, and she, by some miracle of grace, responded. He wrote and asked her to marry him, and she said yes. He was given a few days' leave, before returning to France, and their honeymoon lasted forty-eight hours. Then he left her and crossed the Channel to a rendezvous with the Third Battle of Ypres. It was then the 30th of September, and the battle which cost us nearly 300,000 casualties was a

36

month old. He served in that slough of despond, unhurt, until New Year's Day of 1918, when his battalion was taken out to be re-built and moved to the paler mud of the Somme.

On the Somme, in mid-March, he was waiting eagerly for seven days' leave; but before his turn came Ludendorff on a foggy morning attacked with a local superiority of three to one, and by the end of the month had driven the Fifth Army back to the market-gardens in front of Amiens. My father again survived, and early in April took what was left of his battalion — about eighty or ninety — to St Omer. He saw the prospect of leave renewed, and sent a telegram to my mother to expect him. But now Ludendorff attacked towards Hazebrouck, and my father's ninety ragamuffins became part of a patchwork force, of similar remnants, and entrained once more for the immortal horror of the Salient; where our Portuguese allies, wistful for home, had left a gaping hole.

The patchwork defence held firm, but lost more men in a dozen sprawling, untidy, bitter engagements — and when my father, with forty of his ninety, returned to St Omer, he was promised leave on the 1st of May. He sent another telegram to my mother, who went hurriedly to London to meet him. But he did not arrive. Not till the 4th of May did he appear — for vain alarms had again prevented the leave-ships sailing — and when at last my mother saw him, he was in a very curious state of mind.

My mother knew little of London. Her father was a cheerful, pig-headed extrovert with Boer War medals and a stiff leg who had served on Buller's staff at Colenso and still thought his General a much misunderstood man: he believed in keeping his five daughters at home, in Herefordshire, and when my mother had to make arrangements for what would be, she hoped, a second, long-delayed paragraph in the agonising brevity of her honeymoon, she sought advice of her fellow V.A.D. nurses. They, more worldly-wise than she, unanimously recommended the Regent Palace Hotel: the gayest and most agreeable hotel in London, they said, and just the place for a war-time wedding-trip.

So there my mother went, and waited, waited, not knowing what to do as day after day went by, and still the husband whom she hardly knew — who hardly knew her — did not arrive. But on the morning of the 4th of May a telegram was given her that strangely read: 'Behold your bridegroom cometh Victoria 3.40.' — Such a message was utterly unlike anything my father would normally write, it was wholly out of character, but she went, of course, to Victoria, and because her taxi broke down on the way — another war-time casualty — and it took her long to find another, she arrived half an hour late.

The arrival platform was deserted. A troop-train had indeed come in, strictly on time, at 3.40, but none of its human freight remained. Or so it seemed, and so she thought, until, distracted and incapable of deciding what she had better do, she walked aimlessly, but in a nervous hurry, to the very end of the platform, and there, quite alone, saw an officer sitting on a porter's barrow. His attitude betrayed his utter weariness, but despite the slackness of his tired muscles, his shape and the very demeanour of his lassitude were oddly distinguished — and when, as she approached him, he raised his head, she recognised my father.

'Darling!' she cried. 'Oh, my darling, I'm so sorry! But I'll explain everything later. You're tired, I'll take you with me. There's a taxi waiting. Oh, darling, come with me!'

He stood up, slowly, and looked at her, for a moment, without response. Then he smiled, and said, 'How very kind you are....'

All this my mother told me many years after, when I was grown up. When, in fact, I had come home from Hitler's

38

tedious war, and though my father and I were on indifferent terms, my mother and I were the closest of friends. She found an unfading pleasure, then, in recalling the early years of her marriage....

'He smiled,' she would say, 'and my heart melted to see how tired he was. His cheeks were set and lifeless — oh, like a galantine of chicken — and it was a real effort for him to smile. Even his eyes were dead and lack-lustre. He had eyes like yours, dear, more beautiful than yours, and that day they were like the eyes in an old, over-varnished painting. But he smiled, and I put my arms round his neck to kiss him.

'He seemed surprised, and I couldn't understand why. I kissed him again, and he said, "Charming, charming!" He kissed me on the cheek, and when I smelt his breath I realised he had been drinking. But he didn't smell badly. It wasn't a vulgar smell. It was a champagne, brandy, and cigars smell. But very strong! So I took him by the arm, and looked for a porter. But most of the railway porters then were women, and when I had called one he wouldn't let her carry anything but a knapsack. He had a valise and a very heavy army pack, and these he insisted on carrying himself, and then he gave the woman five shillings, which I thought absurd.

'Well, we got into the taxi, and then, to my surprise — for I thought he was much too tired — he became quite demonstrative. And how pleased I was! How happy! Oh, it was wonderful! But when we came to the Regent Palace Hotel, he was very much surprised, and asked where we were.

'"Have you a room?" he asked.

'"Yes, and a very nice one — with a bath-room."

'"I've never been here before," he said. "When we came to London we always stayed at the Coburg. Though it isn't the Coburg now, is it? They call it the Connaught now, I think. But this is much livelier!"

39

'It was, in fact, very lively: full of officers on leave — the Australians and Canadians making an awful noise — and some very nice, comfortable-looking, good women, but a lot of others who were much smarter and certainly not nearly as good — and a band was playing — and the air was hot, and the sound of all those voices made me a little dizzy.

'Well, when we got to our room, the first thing he did was to open the heavy Army pack he had been carrying — that he had insisted on carrying — and then I saw it was full of champagne and brandy: six bottles of champagne, and four of brandy. We drank a bottle of champagne out of tooth-glasses, and — oh, my dear, I can't go on, can I? All I can say is that I fell madly in love with your father the first moment I saw him, and after two days in the Regent Palace Hotel I was in a shimmer of delight like dragonflies in their ecstasy.

'But he was very naughty! I wasn't used to drinking any-thing at all, and we drank champagne and brandy all the time, and I've never been able to remember what we talked about! I tried, of course, to tell him how much I had missed him — and how I had been waiting for him, day after day — and I do remember being annoyed because he didn't seem to be listening, but wanted to talk about — well, he thought I was beautiful — and I was very young, of course, and when you're young your skin is nice and fresh, and after all those months in the trenches — oh, I could understand how he felt, and I didn't blame him for drinking too much, because in the hospital I had seen what war did to men's minds, as well as to their bodies.

'We went out, next morning, but not for very long. We went to a bank, and we had lunch somewhere — and then we went back to the Regent Palace. We both wanted to. And then, oh then, before anyone could have expected, it was morning — and when I woke up he was standing by the bed, properly dressed and newly shaved — I smelt the soap on his cheeks when he kissed me — and when I asked him what was the matter, and where he was going, he said, with a sort of cold and distant sadness in his voice, "Victoria. The boat-train leaves at twelve."

'I burst into tears. Yes, burst! I'd often read of people "bursting" into tears, and never believed it possible. But that's what I did. Like a fire-hose. And all he did was to kiss me again, and say, "You're the most enchanting cut of Eve I've ever met, and it breaks my heart to leave you. There's something on the mantelpiece to show my gratitude."

'Then he went, and though I jumped out of bed, and followed him to the door, I couldn't go any farther. So I sat on the side of the bed, and cried like an orphan. Cried till I was sick! But then I thought of what he'd said, and wondered what he'd left for me on the mantelpiece.

'There were two vases on it — black unpleasant pieces of pottery — and under one of them a little heap of crumpled, thin, white paper. A little heap of £5 notes. Ten of them!

'That is what he had left for me — and then, immediately, I realised that what I had first suspected was true. When I met him at Victoria, he hadn't recognised me, he didn't know who I was. He had been waiting for his wife — waiting week after week in France and Flanders, then day after day in Calais, and in Calais, after months of battle and weeks of disappointment, he had drunk down frustrated days and crossed the Channel, at last, in a haze where fondest expectation and fiercest disillusion met as if on the edge of a rainbow in an April storm — and when I came at last, late, too late to meet his train, he thought I was a tart, and took what I offered because his wife — the wife he hardly knew, the wife he couldn't remember — had disappointed him and failed him: as so many wives disappointed and failed their soldier-husbands.

'At first — well, it was like falling out of a top-storey window. Utter collapse, and the wind as I went down taking the breath from my mouth! And the cruel, cruel slap on the pavement! But then — I had a fit of the hiccups — and after the hiccups I counted those £5 notes again, and I said to myself, "My God! I'm worth more than I thought! £25 a night!"

'I looked at myself in the mirror, and said, "That's all he saw. He didn't know who you were — he thought you were a tart who picked him up at Victoria — and after a couple of nights in the Regent Palace he leaves you fifty quid!" And do you know, I felt, quite suddenly, like a queen in her splendour! £25 a night, in 1918 when a fiver was really worth something — oh, it gave me such a feeling of confidence. After all, what does any normal woman really want to be? She wants to be a great, successful courtesan! And that's what your darling, wonderful father had told me I was! Worth twenty-five quid a night, just for myself. He made me happy for life!'

I must have heard the story at least a dozen times, for after my father died my mother began to drink rather too much, and grew inclined to repetition; but I always enjoyed it, because her enjoyment in telling it was infectious. Her manner was always vivacious, and though her figure had become commonplace and dumpy her face retained a youthful look to which laughter gave curious reality. She was a delightful, warm-hearted woman, and the gusto with which she tasted the vulgarity of saying 'fifty quid' was irresistible. Her big brown eyes would open wide to wonderment, gleam in naughty delight, and then grow solemn as seriously she added, 'In 1918, when a fiver was really worth something!' When she finished her tale, as she always did, with the assertion that my father's ludicrous mistake and wanton extravagance had made her 'happy for life', she was, I believe, speaking simple truth.

But then her voice would change, her vivacity dim to the quietness of confidential, two-in-a-corner gossip, as she explained: 'But your father, I'm afraid, suffered a lot when he discovered the truth. He never admitted, of course, that there was anything to discover — he was far too much of a gentleman for that. But he must have got a fearful shock when he read my letters! Naturally I said nothing to show that I knew he hadn't recognised me — I simply told him, again and again, of the ecstatic happiness he'd given me. I didn't ever mention the fifty quid! I just wrote love-letters, and he, poor darling, who didn't know he'd been making love to me, could only reply, for a long, long time, on what they called "field postcards". They were cards that the soldiers were given, printed with fairly impersonal sentences, like "I am quite well", or "I have been slightly/seriously/gravely wounded"; or "I have received your letter/parcel/postal-order". And for six weeks all I got from him was a series of these postcards saying "I am quite well" and "I have received your letter".

'The poor dear was trying to work it out, and clear his mind, and get used to the fact that he'd made love to his wife — very expensively — without knowing who she was! And I've always believed that it was worrying about all this that gave him shell-shock, quite as much as being blown-up by some sort of shell or bomb that they called a "Jack Johnson" just after his battalion had taken a very important part of the Hindenburg Line, and practically won the war.

'You must remember that! He was commanding his battalion, and his battalion "played a vital part in the operations": that's in the official history. But your poor father was shell-shocked, and I don't believe he ever quite

43

recovered. He was dear, sweet, and loving to me when he came home, but when you were born he used to stand by your cradle for an hour at a time, looking down at you in utter bewilderment.

'I made him take you for little walks, in your pram, with the idea of compelling him to accept responsibility, as well as making him better acquainted with you; but as often as not he'd come home and say, "What did you tell me the boy's name is?"

'Oh, it was very difficult, but we got on together because I was passionately in love with him, and desperately sorry for him too — he had taken far, far too much of the war on his own shoulders — and he was quite pathetically in love with me, for at least a year, because what he really needed was a nanny — and I was a much nicer nanny than most of them are!

'Yes, it was difficult, but it could have been worse. All that worries me now is that you and he never became so friendly as I had hoped you would — and that he, poor darling, never seemed to recover his spirit. He did deserve to enjoy himself, after all he'd gone through — but he didn't, in spite of all my efforts.'

My father, as I knew him, was a broken, worn-out man; and my mother loved him truly till the day of his death. Thereafter she looked for consolation to drink and religion, and apparently found what she wanted in gin and the Buchmanite theology. She took to gin — plain gin and water was what she liked — with an innocent, astonished pleasure — and to Buchmanism with a humble, shining gratitude that I found infuriating; though for her sake — to preserve her peace of mind — I uttered neither criticism nor complaint. And, to be fair, I must admit it was gin, not Buchmanism, that killed her.

She went to a cocktail party one evening, and found it

more amusing than usual. Her host was a retired Admiral who, remembering his youth in destroyer wardrooms, applauded her taste for gin-and-water, and persuaded her (easily enough) to have two or three too many. She left the party later than she had meant to, and drove her small car — a Morris Minor — with reckless speed to her next appointment; which was a meeting of Buchmanite notabilities in a house some four or five miles away. At a cross-roads where she should have stopped, she failed to, and drove headlong into a Bentley carrying some of the notabilities whom she was going to meet. They were unhurt, except for bruises and a cut or two, but she, alas, died an hour later. She alone was to blame.

It was after her death that I read the last pages of my father's patchy, ill-kept journal. I was unhappy, and bitterly oppressed by the loss of the mother I had doted on. I was inclined to blame my father not only for my own unhappiness, but for his gross failure to live and look after the dear woman who had devoted herself to him. I read his journal with an angry eye alert for confession of weakness; but it was with considerable surprise that I discovered how well aware of it he was, and how sure that the blame for it should be laid, not upon himself and his exhaustion by war, but on a remoter cause.

A month before he died he had written:

I am still perplexed by the utter failure of my life. I spent my youth in earnest study, I was serious, happy, and of good intention. My early manhood I gave to my country's service, and I spent my strength in service. Surely, if God is just, I have deserved a little happiness in my latter years: some small reward of peace and contentment? But no such reward has come my way, and the only reason I can find is in that merciless text, *for I*

*the Lord thy God am a jealous God, and visit the sins of the
fathers upon the children unto the third and fourth generations.*

My father was guilty of a great fault, and though
society forgot it, he never did. I was only ten or eleven
when he died, but I remember him as an unhappy man
who, in the sternest judgment, perhaps deserved his unhappiness. My mother, a very beautiful woman but
often indiscreet, once told me the circumstances of his
disgrace, and though she vigorously defended him, the
story sullied my boyhood. I do not claim that I myself
have been blameless in my life — but I do protest that
my father, by example, by the heritage he left, and by
the mood of mortal failure he bequeathed, was more to
blame, for what I have failed to do, than I myself.

III An Oriental Mishap

IN October, 1888, my grandfather Thomas Vanbrugh, then a Captain in Prince Albert's Regiment of Assam Light Infantry, was on leave in the pleasant hill-station of Shillong, the administrative capital of Assam. He was a good-looking young man with some independent means (and the expectation of more) who enjoyed polo, dancing, shooting duck, hunting big game, and the society of pretty married women whose husbands were busy elsewhere. I can find no evidence that he spent much time or energy on studying the profession of arms, to which he was nominally dedicated, but in his day that neglect was not uncommon, and he appears to have enjoyed the esteem of his senior officers as well as the favour of many friends, both male and female, who — as he did — relieved, whenever possible, the tedium and discomfort of their

47

service in India by their enthusiastic interest in flirtation or shikar.

As a shikari he was much respected; as a 'flirt' — the term is old-fashioned, but with some differences the type remains, I think — he was, by the ladies of the hill-station, regarded with mixed feelings. There were those who praised him for his liveliness, spirit, and address; but others, after brief experience, would have nothing more to do with him. He had, they said, little to commend him but fine words and waltzing; and he could reverse as deftly in one as the other. They complained, in effect, that he was bold in assertion but in action too discreet.

That season, however, there was in Shillong a lady, not long arrived in India, who had already, according to the reckless gossip of a hill-station, driven a young subaltern to suicide and disrupted two previously happy marriages. Her name was Lilian Bellairs, and her husband was the British Resident at the little Hindu kingdom of Balipur on the wild, head-hunting, eastern side of Assam. She was a great beauty — no doubt of that — though there were disapproving or jealous women who said, 'Look at her mouth! I would never trust a woman with a mouth like that.' And others, perhaps wiser, said, 'Look at her eyes. They calculate, and weigh you up, and watch for advantage. They are cold, self-seeking eyes: she is out for all she can get, and I don't like her.'

The men, however, had no such doubts. They were in generous agreement that Lilian was God's gift to Shillong — God's gift to all Assam — and most of them were fortified in their opinion when gradually and cleverly she let it be known that her social connexions were as superior to the dull majority as, more obviously, was her figure. Within a month or so it was common knowledge that her kinship included a Deputy Lieutenant, a Baronet, and the Governor

48

of a Caribbean island. The ladies of Shillong grew increasingly irate, and with Victorian impetuosity the men tumbled over each other to lay their hearts on the doorstep of her bungalow.

My grandfather, Tom Vanbrugh, forgot discretion and fell over head and ears in love with Lilian. She, to all appearances, returned his passion, and they became, for a few weeks, the cherished scandal of Shillong. They rode together on the long, pine-smelling hill-paths of the Khasi highlands. They waltzed together, with grace and skill, in a conspicuous and transparent haze of absorbed self-interest. He drove her home — and from chattering servants the memsahibs may have heard how long he stayed.

Gossip grew like weeds in a wet summer; but to discount gossip there is his diary. My grandfather, in the family habit, wrote a journal that, for the most part, looks very like a game-book: there is repeated account of tigers that measured ten foot six from nose to tail, of elephant shot at six yards distance, of three hundred duck killed in a morning on the Loktak lake in Manipur — but here and there, as if to advertise their peculiar interest, are entries written in dog-Latin. A mongrel, quite ungrammatical, but oddly fluent Latin. These passages refer to a couple of pretty young Khasi girls whom, in the fashion of the time, he had acquired. But of Lilian he writes always in English, with open love and devotion. He needed no obscuring Latin for her because, as I believe, their passion, if not wholly innocent, broke no rules but those of cold prudence. The gossips were wrong again.

Then came the time when Lilian had to return to Balipur and her husband; and say what you like about her lack of discretion, you must acknowledge her hardihood: she had her full share of the strength and bravery common to all the dauntless women who, in those years, lived and sometimes misbehaved in India. When she left Shillong she faced a journey of sixteen days through jungle and wild, mountainous country, and for much of it she was alone, or with no better company than her bearer, her ayah, and the coolies who carried her baggage. Tom Vanbrugh rode the first stage with her, down-hill from Shillong towards the wet plains of Sylhet, but on her second day she sat miserably in a Khasi chair: a tall cane basket with a narrow seat and a foot-rest that a hill-coolie slung across his shoulders, and from which she looked backwards, up at the precipitous mountain-side down which her stinking carrier went jog-trot, lurch and slither, in the growing jungle-heat.

There followed a day in a covered boat, lying sweating under a close thatch while the crew chanted monotonously and thrust against the current. From that to horse-back, and a day when her pony fell lame and they were benighted, lost, but rescued at last by a surprised and only half-sober planter. Day after day, hot and fly-bitten, separated by comfortless nights in lonely dak-bungalows: no company on the roads but naked, spear-carrying Nagas, no habitation but Naga villages on the hill-tops, and no reminder of the comforting British raj that maintained peace on the road but an occasional police thana. And then, at last, where the jungle began to climb the huge green ridges of the Chin Hills, her husband met her, and she rode the last three stages in barbaric splendour on one of the Maharajah's elephants.

The little kingdom of Balipur lay in the midst of the hills, a fertile, well-watered, and populous plain, within natural ramparts and a forest-screen hardly penetrable except where a few steeply climbing native roads threaded the jungle. Some two hundred years before, an unobserved colonial adventure had established a Hindu ruler and his court among the native pagans of the plain, and the present Maharajah claimed, perhaps rightly, to be of Rajput descent. He was a small, unimpressive man, very friendly and good-humoured when he wasn't suffering from one of his periodic fits of angry depression; and Edwin Bellairs was on good terms with him.

The Residency was a vast bungalow, deeply thatched and surrounded by broad verandahs, that stood in a park of several acres with great trees for shade and bright-flowering shrubs and a small lake for ornament. Some two-score servants — not counting gardeners — attended the Resident and his lady, and a dozen chuprassis in long red coats condescended to run messages, but would do no other work. A detachment of sixty men of the Gurkha Rifles, under command of a subadar and two other native officers, guarded the Residency, and behind it was a fairly large village which, with its inhabitants, the Maharajah had presented as a personal gift to Bellairs. He and his wife could not strictly be called lonely in their remoteness; but there was no one, within a hundred miles or so, to whom they could speak English, and only a very few who knew Hindustani.

The outer wall of the Palace rose a few hundred yards from the bungalow; but the Palace was a small city, not a single building. Between the outer and inner walls there were many houses, large and small, and a broad moat; and near the centre of the inner quadrangle was the royal court-yard flanked by the Durbar Hall. It was a shoddy court-yard, with plaster peeling from the arches, and grotesquely out of keeping with the old red fort that filled, with simple, rugged grandeur, its eastern side.

Within the precincts of the Palace there was always work of some kind going on — a new house being built, an old house being demolished — work that was never finished, and never would be, for usually the builder changed his mind, or forgot his intention, or was put to death for some small misdemeanour before his plan could be executed. There was also a temple and a shrine, and always, in every part of the

Palace, a movement of people — except in the heat of afternoon, when it became a huge, untidy dormitory, a somno-
lence of white-clad figures snoring gently in shuttered rooms,
or curled in a doorway, or prone in the shadow of a wall.
The whole population of the plain of Balipur was about
120,000, and Bellairs, who was not without a simple humour,
used to say they all called at the Palace at least once a
month.

The Maharajah had several brothers, or half-brothers, and
most of the State dignitaries were members of his own
family. He had no children — he was known to be impotent
— and the Yuvraj, or Crown Prince, was the brother next to
him in age. The dominating personality at his court, however, was a cousin called the Thakur Sahib, who was the
Senapati, or Commander-in-Chief, of the State forces. There
were other brothers and cousins who held such positions
as Mayor of the Palace, Commander of the Horse, Commander of the Elephants, Keeper of the Roads, and so
forth; and down through the family hierarchy ran a deep
division. To begin with, it was neither bitter nor dangerous;
but it became both. On the one side were the Maharajah
and his younger brothers, on the other the Yuvraj, the
Thakur Sahib, and their adherents. It was in part the easy,
idle good-humour of the Maharajah, in part the moderation
and good sense of the Yuvraj, that prevented open dissension
and kept a rough equipoise; but the advent of Bellairs and
his wife upset the balance.

The fault was not gravely theirs: not primarily theirs, nor
chiefly theirs. Geography and the poor aspirations of the
human heart must bear the larger blame for what happened;
and it needs be emphasised that, for the first year and a half
of their residence in Balipur, Bellairs and his wife behaved
wholly in accordance with their instructions from the
Government of India, and by their friendly behaviour estab-

lished an authority that was recognised alike by the Court
and the farthest village in the State.

As an official, Bellairs was conscientious and tactful; as
a man, he made friends easily, in a country where polo was
traditional and game abundant, by his hard riding and
straight shooting. That Lilian Bellairs enjoyed playing the
great lady of the land is not to be doubted, but also it must be
accepted that she did it very well. She wrote regularly to
Tom Vanbrugh, and Tom kept all her letters. They are
written in that rich yet exasperating convention of letter-
writing which flourished in India in the late 19th century.
Lilian was very sure of herself, and perfectly assured in her
position; but she was equally aware of the bounds of good
taste, beyond which she might not tread. Her descriptions
of duck-shooting and the scenery are full and vivid; she can
evoke the crowded life of the Palace, and of the village that
she and her husband owned. She can be politely humorous
about her ayah, the chuprassis, the difficulties and mishaps
of Oriental house-keeping. She can permit herself to mention her loneliness, but she will not condescend to a description of the sensations of loneliness. When circumstances are
obviously too much for her, she has recourse to a conventional
piety — 'it is God's will' — and that is all. She never speaks
of her real emotions, nor says what she really thinks of the
Princes with whom she goes riding. She will describe,
brightly and in detail, the clothes they wear; but when, for
polo, they exchanged dhotis for tight-legged trousers, she
cannot use that emotive word, but must call them 'con-
tinuations'.

And yet, despite the bonds of her style, you can discern the
energy of her life, her goodwill, and the pleasure she brought
to that confined and ridiculous court among the hills. There
were, in the royal family, a score or so of titular princesses —
girls between the ages of ten and fifteen — and for them she

was always giving parties at which she made them play children's games, or showed them her frocks, and let them use her hair-brushes and try on her hats. When she writes of these activities her formal pages are full of a fluttering awareness of bewildered, giggling, excited girls in their bright saris — their black hair shining, their dark eyes wide with astonishment — and it is quite clear that she was 'good with children' and knew how to let them enjoy themselves.

The Maharajah often visited the Residency, but to preserve his royalty never stayed more than ten minutes. It was difficult to entertain him, because he spoke neither Hindustani nor English, and his religion forbade him to eat or drink in the presence of infidels. His brothers and his cousins were even more frequent guests, and less insistent on formality. Two or three of them would usually come to the children's parties, and Lilian was unable to conceal the fact that some were more welcome than others. The Master of the Elephants, for example, was an uncouth young man who chewed pan supari and 'disgustingly spat red juice all over my nicely raked garden paths'. (In all Lilian's letters this is the one open expression of dislike for her royal neighbours.) That the Thakur Sahib was her favourite is, however, clearly shown; and Bellairs also was more friendly with him than with the others. Two or three times a week they rode together, and the Thakur Sahib, being fluent in Hindustani, could talk freely with them, and showed an intelligent sympathy with their desire to see the country and learn what they could of the life of its people.

After the tragedy there was a great deal of gossip, in Assam and Bengal, about Lilian's relations with the Thakur Sahib; and the more spiteful did not hesitate to accuse her of misbehaviour. But that, I am sure, was mere slander, as idle as it was vicious. In her letters to Tom Vanbrugh she often spoke of him, praising him for his cheerfulness and his skill with a gun; and once she wrote, demurely, 'He is said to have six wives already, and to be courting a seventh. I have seen "the new girl" — she has been to one of my parties — and she is indeed very attractive. Some of his older wives, I daresay, are by now a little past their best.' — That is not the tone of a woman who is secretly in love or enjoying a clandestine affair with the man of whom she writes.

But though, in the narrow sense, there was no impropriety in her friendship with the Thakur Sahib, both she and Bellairs were imprudent in letting it be seen that they preferred his company to that of the other princes. Imprudent, but how natural! They could talk to him as they could talk to no one else; and they were starving for company and friendship. In all their three years in Balipur they had perhaps a score of English visitors: sometimes an official on tour, or an officer of the Gurkha Rifles or the Assam Light Infantry who came for a week's shooting, and once or twice a neighbour who lived, eight days' march away, across the Burmese border. To have maintained, in such a condition of life, an absolute social impartiality — to have shown as much favour to the loutish young Master of the Elephants as to the intelligent and companionable Thakur Sahib — was utterly impossible for a young and lively woman, hardly to be expected in even the most conscientious of civil servants.

But their partiality had lamentable effects. The dignitaries of the little court were suspicious by nature, they had been born into an atmosphere of intrigue, and though each of them was eager for the friendship of the British Resident, they were all secretly afraid of the far-off but overwhelming power of the British Raj, that could at will dislodge them from their privilege. In the growing favour shown to the Thakur Sahib they saw an increasing threat to their own positions, and the old rivalries of the court became bitter.

The Maharajah's party was the more vocal and at first the more active in creating dissension; but the faction of the Yuvraj and the Thakur Sahib was the stronger.

The Maharajah fell into one of his periodical fits of despondency, and for several weeks Bellairs saw nothing of him. His requests for an audience were refused on one pretext after another. His Highness was ill, His Highness was doing puja, His Highness's astrologer said the day was inauspicious. The situation became serious when the Yuvraj, ever tactful, left the Palace and went into camp some thirty miles away, by the lakeside. Then Bellairs, much worried, told Lilian that he thought they should prepare for trouble, and asked her if she would like to have beds made up in the cellars for herself and her ayah. This, in her Victorian hardihood, she refused to permit.

Though so far from any of the main administrative centres, they were not without means of communication. The entrance to the Residency was flanked on the one side by a gate-house, on the other by a small, brick-built telegraph office: the line led across the hills to Bishenchar, ninety-six miles away, where there was half a battalion of the Assam Light Infantry. Bellairs reported his 'sense of discomfort', but felt he had no good reason for asking for troops to be sent in. He advised the subadar commanding his escort to double the sentries and hold a section in readiness: but without ostentation, without advertising preparedness.

For a couple of days nothing happened, and though Bellairs was again refused an audience, and looked in vain for the Thakur Sahib, he found the precincts of the Palace quiet. But on the third night after the departure of the Yuvraj they were wakened, about midnight, by 'a hurricane of shooting' — so Lilian described it — from the Palace, and when they rose and quickly dressed they saw above its roofs and between its houses the glare of torches, and heard, as well as musketry, the beating of drums, wild trumpet-calls, and the shrill roar of excited voices.

The escort turned out — sixty well-drilled sepoys — and Bellairs, with a jemadar in attendance, was about to go boldly to the Palace to investigate — though Lilian, now thoroughly frightened, begged him to wait until daylight — when they were startled by the sudden appearance of about twenty fugitives, running out of the darkness of the carriage-drive, among whom, in the lights of the Residency, they recognised the Maharajah in pitiful dishevelment, and with him two or three of his younger brothers. His Highness was bare-headed, his long hair hanging like a horse's tail, and he wore only a shirt and a torn dhoti. His brothers were in no better shape, and though some of his sepoys carried muskets they had clearly little aptitude and less inclination to defend him.

He had come, said the Maharajah, to seek refuge and safety from a rebellion against his rule that had been instigated by the Yuvraj and planned by the Thakur Sahib. He had escaped from the Palace by a secret passage while his own adherents still fought bravely against the insurgents: but fought without hope against superior numbers. He was in imminent danger — the noise of musketry had already grown less, a sure sign that resistance was almost over — for his life would be forfeit if he fell into the hands of the rebels. Bellairs thought this unlikely, but immediately offered his protection. The Maharajah, in spite of his great distress, contrived to smile and said in his usual, disarming way, 'You have always been most hospitable. I was sure you would not refuse me the shelter of your roof.'

An hour later a crowd of Balipuri sepoys halted by the gate-house, and an officer who was more or less in command demanded news of the Maharajah. A few of his men had already found their way into the grounds, and there was some scuffling before they were thrown out again by the Gurkhas of the escort. Bellairs, who was in the telegraph office, came out and said he would speak to no one but the Thakur Sahib. Half a dozen Gurkhas, with muskets at the ready, stood behind him. The Balipuri officer saw the force of the argument they presented, and sent a message to the Thakur Sahib. He, when he came, was apologetic, and told Bellairs that he had taken action with the greatest reluctance, and for no purpose of ambition. His sole object was to save the state from anarchy. They could no longer tolerate the Maharajah's rule, but they had no personal animosity against him.

'His Highness,' said Bellairs, 'is now under my protection, and I have assured him that his life is in no danger. I think you will agree that I was justified in making this promise when I tell you that he is determined to abdicate, and I have already sent a message to the commander of the troops at Bishenchar, warning him to prepare for His Highness's reception.'

'We have always been good friends, you and I,' said the Thakur Sahib.

'Whether our friendship continues, depends entirely on you,' said Bellairs; and with a fine assumption of confidence, walked back to the Residency.

There he found the Maharajah so forgetful both of rank and religion that he was drinking a glass of warm milk and brandy which Lilian had given him. He would laugh at one moment, weep the next, but through tears and laughter he continued to assert his intention to abdicate at once in favour of his brother the Yuvraj. Bellairs thought his decision too hurried, but realised that His Highness was in no state for argument, and presently persuaded him to sleep. He and his brothers lay in the durbar room, and the sepoys and lesser people who had come with him found such comfort as they needed on a back verandah.

58

In the morning the Maharajah's mood was unchanged, and he was in panic haste to leave Balipur. Messengers were sent to the Palace, and scribes summoned. The instrument of abdication was drawn up, signed and sealed, and delivered to the Thakur Sahib. Permission came for the Maharajah to go, and about midday he left the Residency, carried in a dooly, while his brothers rode beside him and his few frightened sepoys marched behind. An escort of Gurkhas went with him, and Bellairs rode the first few miles and took formal leave of him where the path left the plain and entered the forest. The Thakur Sahib, with a troop of horse, watched his departure from a distance.

On the following day the Yuvraj returned and requested an interview. He told Bellairs, as had the Thakur Sahib, that he had no personal ambition, but he had been forced into rebellion to save his country from progressive misrule and the calamity of increasing faction in every department of the state. He did not intend to claim the throne, but to rule as Regent until his position should be recognised by the Government of India; and he hoped, he said, that Bellairs would report, without prejudice, the fortunes of Balipur under its new government.

In the next few months his action and his good intentions both appeared to be justified. A new energy became apparent in the Palace, a new sense of order and security in the country. Roads and bridges were repaired, dacoity swiftly punished. The State forces were more rigorously drilled, and it seemed to Bellairs that their numbers had increased; but of this he could not be sure. As soldiers the Balipuri sepoys were not to be despised, and most of them had seen action of a sort against their wild neighbours in the hills or raiders from across the Burmese border; but the state of their discipline was such that their training could have been doubled and re-doubled in intensity without rousing any

59

suspicion that they were being prepared for war. Lilian, in her letters, observed that when a Palace sentry was being relieved he still took off his coat and bandolier, and handed them, and his musket, to the newcomer.

She also remarked, unhappily, on the changed demeanour of the Thakur Sahib. He was now not only Commander-in-Chief, but the Regent's principal adviser in civil affairs; and his responsibilities were so heavy that he had no time to go riding with his English friends, and his high spirits were much diminished. He was still friendly, but in a distant, guarded way; and neither he nor the Yuvraj ever came to the children's parties that Lilian continued to give. She now wrote of 'a feeling of tension in the air, as if everybody was waiting for something to happen. The country is much better governed than it was, but I doubt if it is more contented. I certainly am not'. Bellairs, however, reported steady improvement under the new ruler, and advised recognition of his authority.

He told the Yuvraj that he had done so, who asked him if he knew that in Bengal the exiled Maharajah was now complaining that he had been driven from the country, and denied having signed the instrument of abdication.

'He also says that I forcibly disarmed the sepoys who came with him to the Residency,' said Bellairs. 'And so I did, for they weren't to be trusted with fire-arms in the state they were in. But I gave their muskets back to them when they left in the morning, and that he hasn't said.'

'Will the Government of Bengal listen to him?' asked the Yuvraj.

'Not if they listen to me,' said Bellairs.

The Yuvraj appeared to be re-assured, and twice, within the next few days, the Thakur Sahib invited Lilian and her husband to ride with him. But then he fell ill with malaria.

In this prolonged season of dull expectancy — expectancy

of no one knew what — Lilian was suddenly rejuvenated by a
letter from Tom Vanbrugh. He had been promoted, quite
unexpectedly — one of his brother officers was about to
marry the daughter of a rich Calcutta merchant and retire
from the service, and another had unhappily been mauled
by a tiger — and he would soon be coming to command the
companies of his regiment that lay in Bishenchar, only ninety-
six miles away. He was, moreover, entitled to some leave, and
that, if he were invited, he would like to spend in Balipur.

Lilian was overjoyed, and her husband saw no reason
to be displeased. The invitation was promptly sent, and the
next month went quickly in expectation, not so much, I
think, of the man with whom she had waltzed and ridden
and talked of love in Shillong, as simply of someone who
spoke English, someone with whom she and her husband
could be at ease in a common acceptance of language and
ideas: it was that for which they chiefly hungered. Now they
had something to look forward to, a break in the long
monotony of their isolation, and beginning at once to plan
the entertainment of their guest they were re-animated by
their cheerful purpose.

He arrived punctually, at the head of a little train of
followers: batman and groom, bearer and cook, grass-
cutters and baggage coolies. Almost immediately they took
him into camp by the lake, where for a week they went out
in the dusk before morning to wait for the flighting of many
sorts of duck, that came in troops and battalions. They lived
in great contentment in the comfort of a many-tented camp
with a score of servants to look after them; and when they
returned to the Residency there was polo every afternoon —
the Regent and the Thakur Sahib were generous with their
ponies — and Bellairs enjoyed the pleasure, which he had
almost forgotten, of sitting after dinner with a guest and a
decanter of Madeira.

That was the pattern of the first two weeks of Tom Vanbrugh's leave. But then came momentous news that threw Lilian into a confusion of inordinate pleasure and vast anxiety; and when it reached the Palace — by servants' gossip before Bellairs could bring the official tidings — reawakened in the Regent and all his court the fear and suspicion they had felt after the flight of the Maharajah, and which time and the Resident's goodwill had lulled. The Chief Commissioner, Mr Goodbody, was coming to Balipur. Coming immediately, with the Colonel of the Assam Light Infantry and a company of the regiment to support his dignity.

The problems of a hostess filled Lilian with delight and perturbation; but the minds of the Regent and the Thakur Sahib were darkened by the fears with which usurpers live. They would not believe Bellairs when he told them that he knew nothing of the Commissioner's intentions. They did know that the exiled Maharajah, living with friends near Calcutta, was using all the influence he could muster in Bengal to persuade the Government of India to restore him to his kingdom; and the Commissioner, they feared, was coming to prepare his restoration.

A few days later Bellairs was instructed, by telegraph, to inform the Regent that this was not the Commissioner's purpose; but once fear had entered that suspicious mind it was not easy to dispel it. There was no more polo in the afternoon, and the friendly association which Bellairs had so carefully re-built — not wholly, but in part — was shattered again. The Thakur Sahib would not receive him, and his servants made the excuse that malaria had recurred.

At the Residency, however, there was so much preparation to be made for the visitors — as well as Mr Goodbody and Colonel Biddle of the Assam Light Infantry there might well be six or seven other officers — that the political implications of their arrival were somewhat obscured. In a Hindu country it was impossible to obtain beef, and Lilian demanded a couple of sheep. But sheep were hard to find, and she accepted a couple of goats instead: thin creatures which had to be fed like Strasbourg geese for the Commissioner's benefit. They were not hard to fatten — they ate everything they were given — but the day before the Commissioner rode in, one was stolen; and Bellairs was told, by his bearer, that the Thakur Sahib was also laying in provisions, as if to prepare the Palace for a siege.

Word was brought that the Commissioner would make camp, before arrival, some twelve miles away, and Bellairs rode to greet him. He returned in time for dinner, but in no mood to enjoy it. He had to inform the Regent that Mr Goodbody would hold a durbar at ten o'clock on the following morning, and express his wish — with as much force as courtesy could encompass — that the Regent and the Thakur Sahib would attend with all their principal officials. What he could not tell them was that the Regent was to be formally recognised as the ruler of Balipur, but the Thakur Sahib, who was regarded as a trouble-maker and blamed by Government for the rebellion, was to be arrested and banished from the country.

Bellairs dined in a gloomy silence, wrote and despatched his letter to the Regent, and went early to bed. Lilian and Tom Vanbrugh, who had been riding in the late afternoon, did nothing to lighten his foreboding by telling him of the great number of State sepoys they had seen, coming in from several directions, on their way to the Palace. The main road, they said, had been full of them.

Early in the morning, however, the Commissioner was received with proper ceremony. A salute of twelve guns was fired, and at the main gate of the Palace, where the Regent, the Thakur Sahib, and the principal court dignitaries

63

awaited him, a carpet had been spread and there were tables laden with flowers. He was garlanded, according to custom, and made welcome in a speech as flowery as his necklace. He replied briefly, and rode on to the Residency.

An hour later Lilian was happily presiding at a crowded breakfast table. Never before had she entertained so many guests, all of whom spoke English as their native tongue. Lilian — as I have said before — was a great beauty, and the younger officers, already excited by their march into new country, were still more excited by her. For a little while the consciousness of what lay ahead was dissipated by high spirits and loud conversation. The Commissioner and Colonel Biddle, both of whom had an eye for a good-looking woman, paid their hostess extravagant compliments and sat too long at table. There were only two people who did not enjoy the breakfast party: Tom Vanbrugh, who cannot have been pleased to see Lilian courted so warmly by strangers, and so relishing their company; and Bellairs, who had now learnt that it was he who must make formal arrest of his old friend the Thakur Sahib.

He left the others and went out to see that all necessary arrangements had been made. The durbar room was guarded, and all its doors but one were locked. Sepoys of the escort were posted outside, and the company of Assam Light Infantry that had come in with the Commissioner was paraded under its native officers. Beyond the walls their tents showed like a white and orderly village, and here and there the smoke of a fire rose thinly in the hot, still air. But discipline, taut as it seemed, could not quite contain the press and flow of the huge, excited crowd on the road. There were several thousand people pressed closely round the entrance to the Residency — about the gate-house and the telegraph office — and like a protruding fist a close pack of some two or three hundred had forced their way on to the carriage-drive, where a dozen Gurkhas, using the butts of their rifles, with difficulty held them in check. Wandering about the grounds were a few sepoys of the Balipuri army, and a dozen nondescript young men of the rougher sort, whom a havildar was vainly trying to expel. And beyond the mass of people on the road Bellairs could see the red and yellow silk cupolas, fringed with silver, of the great umbrellas that were carried behind the chief dignitaries of the state. The Regent and his officials had arrived, and there was no one to greet them.

Hurriedly Bellairs returned to the Residency to tell the Commissioner he must make haste, and Mr Goodbody unwillingly rose from the breakfast table and took leave of Lilian. The written orders of the Government of India which he had brought had been translated into Balipuri by an interpreter and two of Bellairs' clerks, but they still awaited his signature. He took his time about signing them, and impatiently Bellairs went out again to force his way through the crowd with a havildar and a dozen Gurkhas.

He found the Regent waiting, calm and dignified, under his bright umbrella, with most of his court dignitaries, and behind them a dozen saddle-horses, grooms, and a large, untidy escort of armed men. But the Thakur Sahib was not there.

'He came with me,' said the Regent. 'He was as anxious as I am to pay his respects to the Chief Commissioner. But the heat of the morning sun was too much for him. He has been ill, and he felt his fever returning. So he was compelled to go home. That was a few minutes ago.'

Bellairs felt little doubt that while they were waiting for the Commissioner to finish his breakfast, some of the Balipuri sepoys who had got into the grounds had returned and told the Thakur Sahib of the military preparations for his reception — had, in all probability, exaggerated in Oriental fashion the number of troops on parade — and he, suspicious of the display of force, had retreated while there was still time. But he accepted the Regent's excuse, and conducted him to the Residency. The Commissioner did not come out to meet him, but remained in the durbar room. And when Bellairs told him what had happened, he refused to see the Regent unless the Thakur Sahib were also present.

'Tell him,' he said, 'that I shall ignore this slight to my authority, and postpone the durbar till noon. But then I shall expect to see everyone here whom I have summoned.'

The Regent accepted this rebuff with composure, and Bellairs, holding him in conversation, sent for the horses on which he and his courtiers had ridden from the Palace. They mounted at the steps of the Residency, and to mollify a little the effect of the Commissioner's incivility Bellairs walked with them, at the Regent's stirrup, as far as the gate-house. Gravely they rode away, the umbrella-bearers stepping-out and panting behind; and quickly the crowd dispersed.

A little before noon a message came from the Palace to say that the Thakur Sahib was too ill to leave his bed, and in the circumstances the Regent did not think it necessary to attend the Commissioner. He hoped, however, that in accordance with an arrangement made by Mr Bellairs, the Commissioner would condescend to receive the royal orchestra, which had been promised the honour of playing for him at dinner. With some difficulty Bellairs persuaded Mr Goodbody to send a conciliatory reply, and again postpone the durbar, till eight o'clock on the following morning.

At night Lilian presided at a full table, while the Palace orchestra played a medley of tunes. The bandmaster had had some training in Calcutta, and acquired a repertory that included *A Life on the Ocean Wave* and *Lead, Kindly Light*. The first was received with great hilarity, and twice encored, but the hymn, which was played with barbaric melancholy, was

66

heard in silence and the gaiety of the dinner-party was much impaired.

In the morning the Commissioner, the Colonel and Bellairs again dressed in full uniform for the durbar; but no one at all came from the Palace. Messages were exchanged, to no purpose, and about noon Bellairs went to make a last appeal. He refused to take an escort, saying that in the state of excitement that must prevail he preferred to make no show of force, however small. When Tom Vanbrugh volunteered to go with him, however, he accepted his offer; for Tom had made himself well known and become a popular figure. Lilian, by now deeply alarmed, was loth to let her husband go, and even the younger officers were silent and constrained before the impending crisis.

The precincts of the Palace were crowded with the ragged sepoys of Balipur, who showed no positive hostility, but in a menacing silence surrounded Bellairs and Tom Vanbrugh as they made their way to the inner courtyard by the old fort. There they had to wait some time, while various officials went to and fro, but at last they saw both the Regent and the Thakur Sahib. The latter lay on a day-bed, and certainly appeared to be ill. He refused point-blank to attend a durbar until he had recovered his health, and the Regent declared there was no point in his going, as the Commissioner had already refused to see him. With heavy hearts and troubled minds Bellairs and Tom Vanbrugh again forced their way through the horde of sepoys in the outer parts of the Palace, now a murmurous crowd, and as they went out by the main gate the murmuring rose to shrill cries of defiance. But the road from the Palace to the Residency was empty.

Though deficient in tact, the Commissioner had no lack of courage. He listened to Bellairs' report and said at once, but without bombast, 'When diplomacy fails, we must have

67

recourse to arms. I've had a talk with Colonel Biddle and Captain Heywood' — Heywood commanded the company of Assam Light Infantry — 'and they are confident that by a surprise attack they can force their way into the Palace and take the inner part, the old fort, before those ruffians have had time to gather their wits and stand to arms.'

'It was built for defence, and it's very strongly built,' said Bellairs.

'If we had always weighed the odds, we shouldn't be in India to-day,' said the Colonel.

'There is a moat round the inner part, and they have four mountain guns that we gave the Maharajah — him who's in exile — at the time of his accession.'

'The virtue of surprise,' said Captain Heywood, 'is that you deprive the enemy of his advantages. We'll take those guns before they can fire a shot.'

There was logic on their side — the logic of history, the simple logic of the men who had won India by coolly ignoring difficulties, by an arrogant assurance of their own superiority, and by their shrewd reliance on rapid movement and perfect drill. But Bellairs was thinking of Lilian, and Lilian on the eve of battle had lost some of her composure. Now she readily agreed that beds must be carried down to the cellars — the walls of the Residency were only lath and plaster — for though they might not be needed as a dormitory, they would certainly be required as a dressing-station. On this matter Dr Purcell, the Light Infantry's medical officer, was emphatic; and Lilian was visibly affected by the relish with which he discussed the preparation they must make for casualties.

Her confidence was further shaken when she discovered that her ayah, and most of the other servants, had already deserted them and fled no one knew where. At dinner that night she was quiet and subdued, and afterwards the Commissioner and the Colonel could not persuade her to join them in a game of whist.

They rose long before it was light, and the Commissioner, his secretary, and Lilian went down to the brick-built telegraph office at the roadside. A native clerk sent off a long telegram, and before he had finished they heard the first shots fired. The attack had formed up before dawn, and gone in at first light. To begin with, surprise was rewarded with success, and the sepoys of the Assam Light Infantry, storming the main gate, fought their way without much difficulty to the Thakur Sahib's house, that lay under the north wall. They took both it and a neighbouring building, but failed to find the Thakur Sahib. By then the garrison was roused, and a sort of scrambling counter-attack was made on the captured houses. It was easily repelled, but a subaltern leading eight or ten men towards the inner court-yard, was now beleaguered on a flat roof, overlooked by higher roofs, and a sortie had to be made to pull him out of his dangerous position. It was successful, but another subaltern was badly wounded, and for some time there was a lull in the firing. Then those in the telegraph office heard the crack and boom of an artillery piece and its bursting shell, and knew that one of the mountain guns had been brought into action. When the telegraph babu tried to send another message, he discovered that the line had been cut.

Bellairs, who had gone forward with Colonel Biddle, came back to bring up more ammunition. Tom Vanbrugh, he said, had gone in with the first attack and was now in the Thakur Sahib's house. They were temporarily out of touch, but there was no need to worry. A few wounded had been brought out, and he asked Lilian to go back to the Residency and see that soup or tea was made for them. If she could cut some sandwiches and have them sent up, that would also be useful, he suggested.

69

As she walked back, and went in, Lilian was met by fire from the rear of the house. A bullet smashed a window, and two or three more broke little ragged holes in the thin wall. Then came a proper fusillade, and plaster fell, a lamp was knocked over, a picture hurled askew; and Lilian, on hands and knees, sought refuge in a cellar. The subadar commanding the escort led some of his Gurkhas against the enemy, who had occupied the village behind the Residency — the Bellairs' own private village — and drove them out by setting it on fire. They found new positions under cover of the smoke, however, and when a second attack again dispersed them, they waited for reinforcements and then advanced on a longer front.

Colonel Biddle and the Commissioner came back, and while they were debating the new situation a shell from one of the mountain guns flew low over the roof. Another followed, that also missed. They were persuaded, however, that they could no longer continue their attack on the Palace, but must concentrate their whole force on the Residency; and Captain Heywood was ordered to bring in his forward troops. Under accurate covering fire he again stormed the main gate, and held it until those who held the Thakur Sahib's house, and some nearby positions, could withdraw. Slowly, carrying their wounded with them, they retired to a perimeter round the Residency, and the Balipuri sepoys who had begun to invest it were driven back.

The mountain guns kept up their fire, but without much effect until a shell set a corner of the roof ablaze, and when with great difficulty the flames were subdued, part of the house gaped widely to the sky and every room was full of acrid smoke. A council of war was held, and Colonel Biddle admitted that their strength was insufficient to hold the Residency with assurance and simultaneously mount a new attack with any confidence in success. The morning's optimism had vanished entirely, and glum dismay was apparent on every face. Lilian sat with them, and her presence, so keenly felt, increased their anxiety and aggravated their responsibility.

Then the Commissioner, who had the courage to own his mistakes as well as to face fire, said, 'When force of arms is insufficient, we have to try diplomacy again. I think we must ask for a truce and leave to repair the telegraph, so that we can ask for new instructions to meet a situation that no one foresaw. If you will send for one of your clerks, Bellairs, I shall dictate a letter to the Regent — and then, Colonel, you will be so kind, I hope, as to tell your buglers to sound the Cease Fire?'

This was done, the letter written, and after a little while the Balipuri trumpets replied to the bugles of the Light Infantry. For several hours there was quietness broken only by the agitation of some howler-monkeys in the nearby trees, and while they waited for a reply more casualties were carried down to the cellars, and the subaltern who had been wounded in the morning died. Lilian, who had been nervous and depressed for a day or two, then momentarily panic-stricken when the first bullets struck the house, now showed her mettle. When Dr Purcell asked her to help him she did all that was required of her, though sometimes on the verge of fainting. Lilian at this time — and I say it with no thought of mockery, but in all seriousness — Lilian behaved like a true heroine of her age, a Victorian whose sense of duty lay only skin-deep under her frivolity, and as word went round of what she was doing, the hearts of the young officers — Heywood and another were among the wounded — warmed to her in a devotion that, in its outcome, may have been excessive. Tom Vanbrugh, who had fought with great bravery in the assault on the Palace, admitted later that from now on his love for her became increasingly an obsessive responsibility: that her safety seemed more important than any military objective.

When a reply came to their request for a truce, it appeared that the Regent made it a condition that they surrender their arms; but the interpreter and a babu argued over the translation, and the Commissioner sent another letter in which he suggested that an agreement on terms might be more quickly reached if he and some of his senior officers could meet and discuss the situation with the Regent and his advisers.

They waited an hour, and then the reply came that the Regent welcomed the new suggestion, and would see the Commissioner immediately. Mr Goodbody chose his party. Bellairs must go, and Colonel Biddle. He would take the interpreter, but not his secretary.

Now Lilian's bravery faltered and grew faint, as if she had some premonition of disaster. She pleaded with her husband not to go, and Bellairs said shortly that she must not try to turn him from his duty. The Commissioner spoke gently, and with regret in his voice, to explain that only with the help of Bellairs, and his influence with the Thakur Sahib, could they hope to achieve their purpose. 'And don't think we are running into any sort of danger,' he added. 'If I thought that, I wouldn't be going myself.' He laughed hoarsely, a little self-consciously, and patted her hand; but still her eyes were bright with tears. Then Tom Vanbrugh said, 'I shall go too, and you can depend on me to look after him. I'm the lucky sort, and there'll be no harm done if I'm there.'

This may have comforted her, but she had, in any case, no choice in the matter. No choice but to show composure if she could, walk with them to the gate-house, and there kiss her husband good-bye. She cupped his face in her hands, kissed him full on the lips, and having whispered something that none could hear, kissed him again. With an odd formality he stood back a pace, and saluted her; then, with the others, turned and walked towards the Palace. She watched till they were out of sight, and still, for a few minutes, stood there at the end of the carriage-drive. A subaltern waited to escort her to the Residency — waited, tactfully, a little distance from her — and about the gate-house were a few Gurkhas of the escort. Presently she turned towards the house, the subaltern fell into step beside her, and very slowly they walked back. They had just reached the steps when a shell whistled over the roof, and after a gap of startled silence two more followed in quick succession.

Then, for a few minutes, there was the deepest consternation, for no one knew what had happened, and though all could guess, none chose to declare his fear. Heywood, indeed — his arm in a sling and a bandage round his forehead — began to muster a few of his Light Infantry, and with a cracked assumption of confidence said he would go to the Palace and demand an explanation. A shell went through the roof as he was assembling his troop below the steps, and another, that failed to burst, plunged into the drive and threw up a cloud of dust. Then, from the darkness under the trees, a man came running towards them. It was Tom Vanbrugh, with half his face masked in blood.

Two sepoys held him — he hung between them, exhausted, his arms anchored to their shoulders — while he panted and gasped for breath, and his first words were, 'No one is to go back to the Palace. Not a man!'

Then, when he was more composed, 'They were waiting for us,' he said. 'It was a trap, a deliberate trap. They've got the others — they were waiting inside the gate — but I fought clear. I couldn't help them, you must believe me. They were lost in the crowd, and I couldn't reach them.'

'Weren't you followed?'

'Yes, but they went the wrong way. All but one. He saw me, but I ran him through the throat and left him in a ditch.

— But we can't stay here! They'll attack in the morning, and we can't hold them. I'm in command now, Heywood, and I'm going in to give my orders.'

'Not looking like that,' said Heywood, and sending for a bucket of water and a sponge washed Tom's face, and bandaged the long, shallow sword-cut on his forehead. Then they went in, and when Lilian came up from the cellar her hardihood forsook her. She gave a great cry and collapsed in a chair, weeping.

Tom repeated his story, soberly and in more detail, and said again, 'I am now the senior officer here. I am in command, and I say we must go at once. There is nothing we can do by staying. We haven't the strength to attack, and it's doubtful if we have the strength to defend ourselves. I tell you, we can do no good by staying! But there is one useful thing we can do, and that is to save the life of a very gallant woman. She is our responsibility now, and our only duty is to save her. And that we can only do if we march at once.'

And that, of course, was his fatal error. To say it, and make known his reason for retreat! If he had concealed it, if he had dressed-up his motive in some specious talk about tactical necessity, about rearguard action or a fighting withdrawal, he might have been forgiven. But with Victorian precipitancy, with Victorian romanticism, he proclaimed his motive before witnesses who, at the appropriate time, remembered — or swore they remembered — every word he had said. And probably they did, for they were all of one mind, all in agreement that they were Lilian's bodyguard now, and to save her life was their prime duty and their honour. But before the court martial they had time to think again — time to remember a duty to themselves and their careers — and when, in due solemnity and on oath, they re-

peated Tom's words, so that justice might be done, his words
took on a different sound, a less honourable note.

Of their hasty and miserable retreat there is no need to
say much. Lilian at first refused to go — refused to leave her
husband — and was still sobbing blindly when Tom led her
through the burnt-out village and across fields towards the
road through the jungle and over the hills. There were only
enough doolies for the wounded, and the kahars, the medical
orderlies, carried some, sepoys bore others. Lilian had to
walk, and lost one of her shoes before she had gone a mile.
Gurkhas of the escort — they left fourteen dead behind them
— formed the rearguard, but they were not heavily attacked
till the following morning.

They marched all night and half the next day before they
halted to rest in a Naga village. Their pursuers had not
pressed their attack against the rearguard's disciplined fire.
They marched for two more days, with Lilian in a stupor of
weariness until one of the wounded died, and then, in a
blood-stained dooly, she was carried. On the morning of the
fourth day they met a detachment of troops advancing from
Bishenchar, and their physical hardships came to an end.
But for some of them — for Tom Vanbrugh especially —
their mental torment was only beginning.

Lilian, after recuperating for some weeks in Calcutta, went
home with a Commissioner and his wife who, having been
friends of Mr Goodbody, felt some responsibility towards
her and promised to look after her on the voyage; but Tom
Vanbrugh had to wait in Shillong, idle for many weeks,
till evidence was gathered and the court martial assembled.
And now Shillong seemed a different place. The ladies of
the hill-station were openly hostile, their husbands sober and
reserved. For Tom, by his order to retreat, had brought dis-
honour on the army, and all who served the British raj had

lost face because of him. This became lamentably clear when it was known that the column from Bishenchar went in and stormed the Palace on the very morning of their arrival, taking the Regent prisoner and killing the Thakur Sahib.

By then, it is true, two-thirds of the Balipuri army had gone home to their villages, and the gunners of the mountain battery had spent all their ammunition. But no one bothered to make much of that, and no one but Tom himself had any doubt of the verdict when at last he was formally charged with cowardice and the dereliction of his duty. He heard the evidence against him, and was properly astonished by the meaning given to his honest, simple words. He was allowed to speak for himself, and said little because he thought there was no need to say more. He was told to retire, and when, after only a few minutes, he returned to the court, he was utterly bewildered to see his sword on the table with the point towards him. For he was still convinced that what he had done should have earned him praise, not obloquy.

He too went home — the army had no more use for him — and there his perplexity increased when he found that Lilian was now a popular heroine. Bellairs was dead — the column from Bishenchar had found the bodies of him and his companions in a dry ditch — and Lilian was regarded as the sole survivor of one of those outposts of Empire that were never heard of till they were over-run; when their occupants were momentarily but loudly mourned. Tom took no exception to her fame, but why, why, he demanded, was she honoured and he demeaned for a course of action that had kept them together? He was never truly reconciled to this discrepancy, but he was comforted against the world's injustice when, a year later, Lilian consented to marry him.

She, from the day she arrived in Calcutta, had never ceased to protest her gratitude to him. She cared nothing for official or popular opinion, she knew that he had saved her

life and she remembered that he had gone voluntarily with
Bellairs on his last mission; and that was enough for her.
Throughout that wretched year she was the only person who
really believed that what he had done was right; and not the
least of her bravery — though perhaps it savoured of
egotism — was the constancy with which she affirmed her
opinion.

So they married, and in due time she bore him a son and
a daughter, of whom the former, in the manner I have re-
lated, became my father, while the latter lived a speculative
life on the continent and in the ripeness of time died in Nice.
— It must not be thought, however, that Lilian entered a
social martyrdom with marriage, for by then Tom's father
was dead, and as his older brother had lately been drowned
while attempting to sail an over-canvased yacht to Norway,
Tom came into a very comfortable estate. With that to
obliterate it, his neighbours soon forgot the story of his court
martial and disgrace, and so far as they could see my grandfather lived a happy and contented life. But within the
family it was recognised that his recurrent moods of black
misery were due to his fadeless memory of the injustice that
brought his promising career to its untimely end.

This he frankly admitted when the South African war
broke out. 'Here,' he said, 'is my chance to redeem myself.'
He was thirty-nine by then, and Lilian had grown in
authority as he in years. But in spite of his age, and her
wrath and anguish, he insisted on having his own way. He
enlisted in a Fusilier regiment, and a year later wrote his last
letter to his beloved wife.

We are now Mounted Infantry [he wrote] and I am a
corporal. I am lean as a rake, brown as a brick, slightly
lousy, and almost happy. This, of course, is a ridiculous
state of affairs, for if I had had my rights I should now be

a Brigadier-General at least. But I have a suspicion that I was never meant to be a success. The dice were loaded against me from the start. I remember — how well! — my old booby of a father, and that dreadful day when he covered us all with shame. Oh, what shame! It haunted me for years, and I think it may have left me a little un-balanced in judgment, so I might never have justified promotion to a really responsible rank. I've been a failure — incontestably a failure — but in my failure I have been more than recompensed by the miracle of winning your love. No one since the world began has ever loved more deeply than I love you, nor held to his heart a more lovely, kind, and noble woman. If I lived a thousand years, serving you every year, I should still be in your debt — and so, my dear, though I have not in a worldly way been successful, in a more blessed way I have been lucky far beyond my deserts. That, perhaps, is why I can now say that as a corporal of Mounted In-fantry — a little lousy and dog-tired — I am relatively happy. And if you think it ignoble of me to find happi-ness in so humble a state, you must blame my old booby of a father. It was he who built weakness into me — and God who sent you to mollify the hurt.

Two days later he was killed by a Boer sniper, but Lilian lived till 1930, when I was twelve. My grandfather died in the assurance that she had been the perfect wife, and I live in the knowledge that she was the ideal grandmother. — Dear Lilian, I still have all those wonderful letters you wrote. And I cried for days when you died.

IV Collapse of a Victorian

THE 'old booby' — Tom's father — was Eustace Vanbrugh, born in 1834.

That was the year when the Houses of Parliament burnt
down; but even so plain a portent failed to impress the ruling
classes, and Parliament passed a Poor Law Amendment Act
which, by re-establishing the workhouse, made poverty
punishable by imprisonment. From the economist's point
of view it seemed an admirable measure; but it was out of
touch with reality. The besotted poor refused to take warning, and in consequence lost their freedom and put up the
rates. — Now if the elected rulers of the richest and most
powerful country in the world were as addle-pated as that,
what were the odds on a simple country gentleman who
called himself 'a Whig, and proud of it'?

But he is not a subject for our pity. Far from it! He had advantages that we have never known, and never shall; and I don't mean only material advantages, though they, in the estimate of his contemporaries, were something more than respectable, and by our standards almost fabulous. His father — of whom I shall have more to say presently — had fallen heir, while still a boy, to a large estate in the county of Somerset and industrial property, worth more, in the city of Bristol. He did not marry till he was in his middle thirties, but then quickly begot six children, of whom five were girls. From infancy, then, Eustace entered a domain of great wealth in which he was sustained by the favour of a strong-minded mother and the admiration of five sisters almost as handsome as himself.

The house in which he was born no longer stands. He himself ruined it past hope of repair by a sudden enthusiasm, in the last years of his life, for the architecture of the Gothic revival; the transformation from old plain Georgian to neo-Perpendicular was aggravated, indeed, by the addition of some Venetian motifs. Most mercifully it was hit by an errant bomber in a German raid on Bristol, during the late war, and the resulting fire left nothing but a blackened shell. It had long since passed out of our family. Eustace had two sons, Henry and Tom, and Henry sold the property immediately after his father's death, partly because he disliked intensely the grandiose reconstruction, partly because he, as well as Tom, had been so shamed by his father's behaviour that he could not endure to live in the neighbourhood which had witnessed it. He bought a much smaller estate near Melbury. It was this that Tom fell heir to, after Henry was drowned; and in what had been the dower house on the new property my father lived.

My purpose, however, is not to tell of lost grandeur — nothing so commonplace as that — but of grandeur clowning on its apogee; and here, for a start, are two pictures to illustrate the tale.

First, the old plain Georgian house: a big house, with an added wing on either side — a house that needed, for the maintenance of proper state and comfort, a steward within as well as a land-steward without, a *valet de chambre*, a clerk of the kitchen as well as a clerk of the stables, a chef, a con-fectioner and a baker, a Scotch gardener to dragoon the lesser gardeners and a sober butler to look after the port and the plate and half a dozen footmen; a groom of the chambers for the furniture, a coachman and grooms of a burlier sort for the horses; a lady's maid, a housekeeper, and a whole nunnery (all too permeable) of housemaids, laundry-maids, dairy-maids and scullery-maids. There was a community, a hierarchy and a society within that house, and Eustace grew to manhood as its Heir Apparent and Crown Prince. In proportion to the whole population of England domestic service once employed as many as the civil service does to-day; and what is the civil service but the old domestic service writ large, aggrandised, promoted and set on high to take revenge on its former masters? — But enough of that. There's no room for bitterness here. I am past all bitterness.

So, then, to the second picture: and that is of Eustace at the age of nineteen or twenty. A portrait of a stylish, dandy-fied young man with long hair gleaming with Macassar's oil and carefully disarranged, a collar that comes up above his chin, and an elaborate neckcloth, a flowered silk waist-coat, and generously cut lapels. The eyes are romantically dark, the mouth is passionate, the nose already a formidable promontory — and noses develop with the years, noses (if there is anything in them) ripen, grow harsh or mellow, ex-pose the growing character. And Eustace's nose, at nineteen or twenty, is the earnest, questing nose of an enthusiast: long, aggressive, with a nostril like that of a rocking-horse.

F
81

He had first shown his quality at the age of seven or eight, when he declared himself an adherent of the Oxford Movement. He had, of course, been brought up with a sound knowledge of revealed religion, and by his seventh birthday knew all about Abraham and Isaac, and Lot's Wife, and Moses; he knew the Articles of his Belief as taught in the Anglican catechism, his duty towards God and his neighbour, and the meaning of the Sacraments. He was, more-

Because a tale of relationships always seems more complicated than it is, I have added this diagram of those branches of my family tree of which I have been writing.

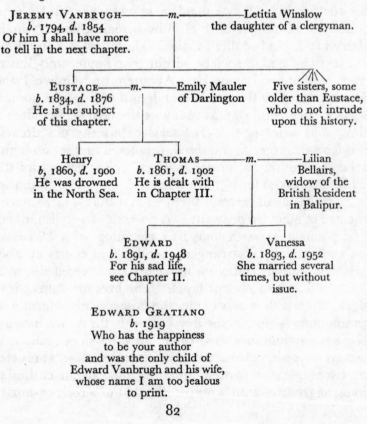

JEREMY VANBRUGH————m.————Letitia Winslow
b. 1794, d. 1854   the daughter of a clergyman.
Of him I shall have more
to tell in the next chapter.

EUSTACE————m.————Emily Mauler   Five sisters, some
b. 1834, d. 1876   of Darlington   older than Eustace,
He is the subject   who do not intrude
of this chapter.   upon this history.

Henry   THOMAS————m.————Lilian
b, 1860, d. 1900   b. 1861, d. 1902   Bellairs,
He was drowned   He is dealt with   widow of the
in the North Sea.   in Chapter III.   British Resident
                                          in Balipur.

EDWARD   Vanessa
b. 1891, d. 1948   b. 1893, d. 1952
For his sad life,   She married several
see Chapter II.   times, but without
                            issue.

EDWARD GRATIANO
b. 1919
Who has the happiness
to be your author
and was the only child of
Edward Vanbrugh and his wife,
whose name I am too jealous
to print.

82

over, fully aware of his own importance and responsibilities in a world created for a divinely ordained purpose. But he was dissatisfied — as the pioneers of the Movement had been — with the assurances of his own, merely human mind, and felt that a personal conviction of salvation was not enough: he wanted the comfort and the romantic vision of an undying, undeviating society lighted through the ages by the fire that the Apostles kindled and the faithful had fed with their discipline from generation to generation.

He found the nucleus or promise of what he needed in Keble's famous sermon on *National Apostasy*, a copy of which his mother gave him, and at his urgent request she then procured from a bookseller a complete set of *Tracts for the Times*. For some months he applied himself with great spirit to their exposition of patristic theology and the Church's divine prerogative, but shortly before his eighth birthday his mother told him, as kindly as she could, that Tract No. 90 — which had just arrived — was likely to prove obnoxious, not only to one of his tender years, but to every self-respecting English Protestant.

Eustace on the nursery floor stamped first one foot, then the other, and demanded instant possession of it. He had a piercing voice, an inflammable temper. His emotion infected his sisters, the oldest of whom was twelve; but even those senior in age recognised his position as heir, and a deafening chorus of five young female voices presently joined him in protest against maternal authority. A nursemaid or two and some of the younger housemaids were attracted by the uproar, and swelled it with their weeping. A couple of footmen came to help, another followed the groom of the chambers carrying a large armchair, newly repaired, that was offered invitingly but unavailingly for Mrs Vanbrugh's greater comfort; and the housekeeper panted in with a jangle of keys and a slight smell of hartshorn. Then Mr

Vanbrugh arrived, and sat in the chair which had been brought for his wife.

'I came to ask,' he said — and then fell as quiet as the rest of them, for in the middle of a sentence he often forgot how he had meant to finish it. Every voice had immediately been silenced by his appearance, because Mr Vanbrugh sometimes had fits of violence and would throw a Chinese vase through the window or box a footman's ears. But now he sat with a look of perplexity in his bright, protruding blue eyes, with a childish bewilderment in the sagging lines of his brick-red face that was so curiously decorated with wens and nodules and studs of pink tissue.

Then, quite suddenly remembering the purpose of his visit, 'I came,' he said, 'because there was so much noise up here. Or wasn't there?'

'Yes, Mr Vanbrugh, I fear there was,' said his wife, 'and I am heartily sorry for it.'

'Ah!' he said. 'I thought so. You can't fool me.' And with a grimace of cunning self-satisfaction he looked very steadily at Eustace, his only son, who stood surrounded by five tear-stained little girls in the centre of the now embarrassed group of servants.

'And what,' he asked, 'is the occasion for this gathering? Is it a prayer-meeting?'

'Indeed, Mr Vanbrugh, it might become something of that sort,' said his wife.

'Well, then, let us go down and leave them to it,' he said. 'For we are getting too old for frivolity. Come along, come along.'

Unobtrusively, but with a sigh, Mrs Vanbrugh gave Eustace her copy of Tract No. 90, and taking her impatient husband by the arm, led him away. The servants followed, and Eustace settled down to read the tract to his sisters.

He was one of the minority of devout Protestants who did not find it offensive. He was, indeed, very pleased with Newman's discovery that the Thirty Nine Articles were directed, not against the tenets of the Roman Church, but against popular error. He had, at that time, a great distaste for any sort of error that could be called 'popular', and for the next few years he thought with increasing kindliness of Papal authority, he showed a keen interest in the matter of vestments, and anxiously awaited tidings of Newman's next step. When, in 1845, he was formally received into the Catholic Church, Eustace was tempted to follow his example, and undoubtedly would have insisted on receiving instruction had his inclinations been opposed in any way.

But his mother, who had learnt her lesson, showed the most tender interest in all he told her, and his tutor, a neighbouring clergyman who was a great admirer of good writing, encouraged him to study Newman's style. With so much favour from his elders, he grew doubtful of their purpose and his own judgment, and discreetly postponing his conversion for two or three years, acquired in that time a belated knowledge of the writings of Archbishop Whately that finally precluded it.

He made the important discovery that a form of faith which required a mystical apprehension as well as intellectual application was not well suited to his nature, and not suited at all to the majority of his fellow-Englishmen. The ultimate condemnation of Newman, of his habit of thought and the demands made by such a habit, was that they were 'un-English'; whereas Whately with his good rough logic, his practical Christianity, his blunt refusal to see anything better than superstition in Romanism, anything more than sentimentality in the preaching of the Low Church clergy — why, Whately was a proper Englishman!

At Oxford Whately had gone about in a tall white hat, a

rough white coat, with a great white dog at heel — and surely that was the true English style? Conspicuous, independent, and sensibly prepared for the worst of weather. Now he was in Dublin, instilling a stern but kindly discipline into the raggle-raggle Irish — and what could be more typical of English benignity than that? A practical faith very comfortably at home in a broad and practical mind: that was the example the Archbishop set, and Eustace at seventeen saw with increasing clarity the advantages of being broad-minded. His faith was untroubled, now that he had turned away from Roman extravagance, and he could well afford a greater breadth of sympathy, of interest and speculation, than he had previously allowed himself.

He went up to the university, then, in the proper mood to enjoy its varied company and accept what benefits it might offer; and in his second year, when Oxford broad-mindedly resolved to admit dissenters to its degrees, he met a young man called Alfred Mauler whose father was a wealthy ironmaster in Darlington. They found in each other a strange affinity — they were both very serious young men — and against all probability became great friends. To begin with, they could hardly understand each other's speech; for Eustace spoke in the broad, slow style of Somerset, and Mauler in the hard-biting roughness of the north. When that difficulty grew less, Eustace was deeply shocked to learn that Mauler and his family not only professed the social philosophy of the Utilitarians, but the religious faith (if such it could be called) of the Unitarians.

His first impulse was to tell Mauler, with all the courtesy he could muster, that they had better not meet again; for he was profoundly repelled by the thought of further association with one whose ideals were those of the tradesman, and his theology so heretical — no better than a Mahomedan! But then he recalled his recently acquired *broad-mindedness*; and realised that now he could put it to the proof. He had, more-over, the natural curiosity of youth, and could not repress an almost prurient desire to know something of the strange, anomalous life of a Unitarian and a Utilitarian. His friend-ship with Alfred Mauler was not broken, but continued and grew closer; with unexpected results for both of them.

Eustace told Mauler of his former enthusiasm for the Tractarians, and his passing temptation to follow Newman into the Church of Rome. Mauler, curious in turn, set him-self a new course of reading, and presently found temptation irresistible. The consequence was that two years later his father the ironmaster — unconsciously plagiarising Disraeli — complained bitterly to his friends in Darlington: 'I sent my boy to the university to make him a gentleman — and all I've done is make him a Roman Catholic!'

Before this happened Mauler had invited Eustace to spend a holiday with him in Darlington, where Eustace fell in love at first sight with his sister Emily. More strangely, he con-ceived a romantic admiration for the scarred and stricken landscape of the north, that he now saw for the first time, and was deeply moved by the prodigious noise and smoke and flame of modern industry.

In the din of a foundry, under a pall of coal-dust, he shouted with excitement, and exclaimed at the top of his voice — for otherwise he would not have been heard — 'But this is a battle-field! Here battles are being fought of greater moment than anywhere Wellington or Marlborough commanded!'

His friend's father, the old ironmaster, was equally moved. He, shouting too, replied, 'These battles we're fighting are battles for a new world. A better, richer world where energy and righteousness will always be free to win great rewards of happiness and prosperity. And we are winning our battles, Mr Vanbrugh. Victory is in sight!'

Grimy and formidable, as grimy in aspect as the soldiers in any hard-fought campaign, the ironmaster's labourers went to and fro, and the ironmaster encouraged them with hearty cries of approval or abuse. At night he and Eustace sat late over their port, and such was their mutual regard that when, on a second visit, Eustace made a formal proposal for Emily's hand, the differences of faith and philosophy that might have separated the two families were overlooked, and a marriage was arranged for the following June. Emily herself found nothing in the Anglican Church and its ritual that could offend a really sensible girl, but much to recommend them. Eustace, now in hot haste for marriage, thought the taking of a degree would do nothing to increase his aptitude for being a husband, and did not return to Oxford.

His father, whose wits had been wandering for several years, was utterly perplexed by the excitement that now filled his house, and died, most opportunely, of a pneumonia after losing his way in his own grounds and falling into an artificial lake. The wedding was postponed for a month, and then Eustace, embracing his bride and his new responsibilities with his customary ardour, entered his heritage in the stern assurance that by continuing in a life of unswerving rectitude he would reap such happiness as he deserved from God's benevolence.

His mother, with all her daughters, went to live in Bath, and Emily, taking full command of her numerous household, quickly showed her northern shrewdness and her native thrift. There were far too many servants in the house, she declared, and many of them did nothing but make work for the others. She proposed to dismiss ten or a dozen immediately; and Eustace, though a little tempted by the thought of reducing his expenses, was much alarmed by the prospect of a household so diminished that it might lose him the respect of his neighbours. He had as large a fortune as he needed, but he could easily enjoy more respect; and so, most opportunely, he remembered the philosophy in which Emily had been brought up, and reminded her of it.

'Though you have now come to live in Somerset,' he said, 'you must not forget everything you were taught in Durham. I am thinking, in particular, of Jeremy Bentham, that great moralist and Utilitarian, who so firmly believed that the legislator's prime duty was to seek "the greatest happiness of the greatest number". Now if you apply this rule to your own household you will see that the servants must be considered as well as my purse. If you sent a dozen of them packing I might benefit, in a very small way, but they would suffer in a large way; and the happiness of an appreciable majority would be much diminished. Then, too, you must think of our neighbours, and of their discomfort if they came to dinner and we had not enough footmen to serve them as they are accustomed to being served; or of their disappointment if they found the gardens neglected because you had dismissed a few gardeners. I applaud, my dear Emily, the interest you take in domestic management, but in this, if in nothing else, I beg you still to adhere to Utilitarian principles.'

Emily thanked him for his advice, and without mentioning the matter again paid-off the clerk of the kitchen and several redundant housemaids, dairy-maids, and scullery-maids. She was tireless in her social duties, and within a few years was so familiar with every respectable family for thirty miles around that she was able to find suitable husbands for all Eustace's sisters. His mother, however, continued to live in Bath, where for some years she anxiously discussed, with doctors and ladies of her acquaintance, the sad topics of sterility and the barren womb.

For in one aspect of her duty, Emily failed. Year followed year, and the nursery still was empty, the nursery door was closed. During this time there were, I am sure, innumerable consultations and family colloquies — the latest medical theories were exchanged, the oldest superstitions were canvassed — ancient midwives were listened to, and there was a wild suggestion that Mr Braid, a hypnotist then practising in Manchester, might be useful. But of what was said on these occasions, of what was attempted and what was done, I can tell nothing. All I know is what happened — and nothing happened to repair the shame of the empty nursery until the year 1860.

Eustace, however, contrived to look as if he were the father of a numerous family: he became portly, stately, grave and solemn. Though he had gladly accepted them, the weight of his responsibilities, of his great wealth and innumerable obligations, settled heavily on his shoulders and within two or three years compressed the springs of youth into the slow and solid structure of middle age. He had never, of course, been much aware of his youth — never sown a wilder oat than his little affair with Newman — and because he had done nothing to encourage youth, it readily deserted him. But the major reason for the rapid change in his appearance was that he desired it: his sense of propriety told him that a man in his position should look ponderous enough to balance it — and so vigorous was his mind that he quickly achieved his aim.

Orderly, devout, and intensely serious: such was his life, and the life of all the better sort in England — for did they not know that every one of their actions was of significance in the living world, and might be of more significance in the next? They had pride in their own capacity, seeing the evidence of it on all sides; and being well aware that prosperity is the natural reward of virtue, they took care to drill and exercise their virtue in family prayers and regular attendance at church. They knew how to reconcile science with religion, and there were even those — among the Liberals — who could detect a religious element in politics.

Though Eustace had now less time for reading, he did not abandon the habit, and still retained his lively interest in all that was new. He read, with close attention, the Scotch geologist Lyell, and learnt from him — without being greatly shocked — that man might have a longer history than the five or six thousand years with which he was usually credited. He read something of Faraday, and discovered that knowledge of the material world was bursting the seams of the old coat that had so long confined it. He read *In Memoriam*, and gravely acknowledged the possibility that Christian faith might live 'in honest doubt' of personal immortality — but if such doubt affected him, he showed no sign of it: no sign of perturbation.

It is, however, quite certain that such reading prepared him, perhaps unconsciously, for the great experience that was to shatter his life and bring the shards of his massive dignity tumbling down upon him like the hewn stones of Gaza on blind Samson's head and shoulders. This calamitous experience — or, more accurately, the warning announcement of it — occurred in the year 1859.

In the early evening of the last day in November the butler brought Emily his master's compliments, and begged her to excuse him from dining with her.

'Why,' said Emily, 'I hope Mr Vanbrugh is not ill?'

'No, madam. He has told me to bring him a chop and a bottle of port in the library.'

'In the library?'

'He is reading a book, madam.'

'It must be a remarkable book, if he prefers it to my company.'

'He appears very intent on it, madam.'

'Then give Mr Vanbrugh *my* compliments, and tell him I am equally befriended with Mr Tennyson's *Idylls of the King*.'

'Very well, madam.'

'And I too will have a chop — and a bottle of claret. In my own sitting-room.'

'Yes, madam.'

Some two or three hours later, Eustace came to Emily's sitting-room, entered a little abruptly, carrying the book he had been reading, and was followed by a footman bearing a tray on which were two glasses and a bottle of champagne. Emily, who had been dozing, picked up her volume of Tennyson and looked at her husband, at first with surprise, then with alarm. He stood swaying to-and-fro — it was obvious that he was not quite sober, but that did not frighten her: it was his expression, and the small, stertorous, choking noises that escaped his trembling lips. Nor did her fear grow less when she realised he was laughing; for he was rarely given to emotion of that sort.

'Oh, Mr Vanbrugh, what is the matter?' she cried. 'And why has Thomas brought a bottle of champagne?'

'To drink, of course. We're going to drink it all!' And now, as if till then he had been practising, or tuning-up, Eustace laughed openly, loudly, and went on laughing for at least half a minute. 'Oh, it's a capital joke!' he exclaimed.

'But what *is* the joke, Mr Vanbrugh?'

'Everything! The whole of creation. You and I, my dear Emily. Why, do you know this — '

He choked again, as laughter came swelling from his heart, and with an unsteady hand poured champagne into the two glasses.

'I think I should not take any,' said Emily. 'I have already drunk a little claret, Mr Vanbrugh.'

'And I have drunk a lot of port, and now I'm going to drink champagne. Because, my dear Emily, we have been set free! Our monstrous prison has collapsed, the floor has melted, and the roof of terror's fallen in. The keeper of the gaol has been dismissed — oh, better than that. Better far! Do you know this, Emily? *He never existed!*'

'For heaven's sake, Mr Vanbrugh, what are you talking about?'

'I'm talking about champagne. Now drink it off!'

And there, unfortunately, we must leave them. What happened next, and what next was said, we do not know. For at that moment Eustace, presumably hearing some small noise, took it into his head that the footman who had carried the champagne had stayed on the other side of the door to listen to the conversation of his betters, or watch them through the keyhole. — He walked quickly to the door, opened it, and found his suspicion verified. He kicked the fellow downstairs, and the following morning Thomas told the butler all he had heard — and the butler told the housekeeper, who took the first opportunity to tell old Mrs Vanbrugh, who promptly wrote to her eldest daughter and gave her a full account of the matter.

All that can be added, with truth and certainty, to the footman's *reportage* is that on the following morning a housemaid found, in Emily's sitting-room, an empty champagne bottle, and on the floor two steel hoops from Emily's crinoline lying beside a copy, brand-new from the bookseller, of *The Origin of Species* by Charles Darwin.

Enthusiasm — serious enthusiasm or enthusiastic seriousness — was, of course, the great fault in Eustace's character. It was typical of his age, but Eustace carried it to excess. To me, seeing him from a distance, it is clear enough that he had shouldered too great a burden, or too many burdens, and when he found them intolerable seized the first excuse for pitching the whole lot overboard, from God to public opinion, into a deep blue sea of total irresponsibility.

And this also was truly *Eustacian*, that he found his excuse in that eminently serious work, *The Origin of Species*. Very few of his contemporaries can have discovered in Darwin an excuse for light-heartedness; but Eustace, because his enthusiasm was more intense, or ever-ready, than theirs, at once perceived the releasing magic of the phrase 'natural selection' — its absolute contradiction of the divine ordinance that had imposed on him a many-sided fear and chained him to responsibility — and as ardently as he had plucked the lilies of revelation from the Tractarians, so now, in this new dawn of enlightenment, he gathered the blackberries of freedom from Darwin's thorny argument.

But Emily, though for a little while she had been swept from her moorings by the exuberance of her husband's eloquence — and by the champagne that he had insisted on her drinking after (if the butler spoke truth) she had drunk all but a glass of a bottle of claret — Emily, under the frosty sun of a December morning, was sceptical and said she must read the book for herself and form her own opinion of it.

She read it carefully, and then, perhaps too stubbornly, said, 'I cannot see that it makes any difference at all. For if living creatures were endowed with the faculty of selection, it must have been God who endowed them. And surely, Mr. Vanbrugh, that does not diminish, but rather aggravates our responsibility?'

'Pooh, pooh,' said Eustace. 'Either you can't understand it, or you're equivocating. The fact of the matter is that Darwin's let the cat out of the bag, and nothing you or anyone else can say will put it back.' And as if to show that he too had escaped confinement, he rang for a pint of champagne.

Within a year or two Eustace became a scandal and a byword in the west of England. His opinions were offensive to the majority, and he insisted on uttering them. He declared his apostasy and exhibited his dissipation. He who had been a pattern to the young became a warning and a menace; and what made him more obnoxious was the evident enjoyment he now found in life.

In his own house, indeed, he was forgiven much, and acquired a new, illogical, and yet natural authority when Emily was at last brought to bed and presented Eustace with an heir. This happy event coincided with the first partridge-shoot of the year. Eustace had invited a dozen of his neighbours, but such was the hostility of the county that only three of his former friends accepted the invitation. They, however, had uncommonly good sport — though the summer of 1860 had been wet and stormy — and stayed to drink young Henry's health with a kindliness that waxed warmer as the hours grew later.

In his new habit of conviviality Eustace became less exclusive than he had been, and in Bristol — where he had large interests — he acquired several acquaintances of a sort he would previously have thought far below his notice. One of these was a learned but rascally old Scot called Argo: a man of sixty or so, a graduate of Edinburgh University, who was employed in the counting-house of a firm of tobacco importers. Argo had led a roving life as schoolmaster, sailor, and planter in America. As a young man, soon tired of teaching in a Scotch grammar school, he had gone as tutor to a nobleman's castle in Saxony; and from there to St Petersburg, then to Odessa. He had left Odessa in a hurry, and becoming friendly with the captain of the ship in which he escaped had remained with him for several voyages, serving as supercargo. Another ship took him to West Africa, where he spent some years as a trader, before taking passage to the Carolinas under the American flag — 'And under hatches,' he would say, 'there were a few blacks whom we carried by friendly agreement with their chief.'

'But England's the best country in the world,' he declared

95

— this on his first meeting with Eustace — 'better than Scotland, for me at any rate, for there's too much competition there, too many of my own sort, and it's a quiet life I want now. A quiet life, and a comfortable house, and room for my books.'

He had read widely, and with a bottle beside him could discuss Malthus and Bentham, Pusey and Newman — and to Eustace's exceeding pleasure, Lyell and Darwin. He, like Eustace, believed firmly in evolution and the hypothesis of natural selection; and as if they were conspirators together, each in possession of the code, both had marked and memorised Darwin's assertion that now 'light will be thrown on the origin of man and his history.'

It was at their second or third meeting that Argo said, 'I could help him in that matter, if ever he cared to ask me.'

'Do you think negroes are of our species?'

'We all came down from the trees,' said Argo, 'but some of us were quicker than others.'

'I am not sure I understand you.'

'There's a God-forsaken place called Benguela, in Portuguese Angola, where I had no right to be, though I stayed there three months,' said Argo. 'I went up-country, farther than the Portuguese had been, and it so happened that I became friendly with an old chief by the simple expedient of saving his life. Oh, it was simple enough. He had a blockage of the kidneys, and I had a case or two of gin: the irresistible force met the immovable object, and all was well again. And then, in pure gratitude, he told me about the Pongos, and showed me the skeleton of one of them, which was his great treasure.'

'The Pongos?'

'That's the word. They live in the forest, and they're bigger than a man. Hollow-eyed, the face and hands without hair, and though they walk on their two feet they've no calf to the leg. They're brown in colour, very hairy about the body, and live on fruit and young plants. They sleep in the trees, and though they have no speech they'll combine to kill an elephant. They're just great apes — but in my opinion they're your ancestors and mine; distant ancestors, you'll understand. But near ancestors of the black men.'

To Eustace this tale of the pongos — now more commonly called gorillas — was pure enchantment. It completed his sense of liberation from the dire responsibilities of humankind; and also, I think, from the dull routine of modern life. His second son, Tom, was born some fifteen months after Henry's birth, and about the same time several maids employed in the house — or in the laundry or the dairy — had to be sent home and suitably provided for. Eustace, I fancy, had been enjoying a vivid *recherche du temps perdu* in which he saw himself swinging from branch to branch of the Tree of Life as gloriously free as a pongo in the Equatorial forest.

He, who could trace his ancestry back to four beds only, had always been jealous of his noble neighbours whose family trees were rooted in Plantagenet or Angevin soil — some, indeed, claimed Saxon origin — and to discover a source for his blood so infinitely remote as the groves of Africa gave him a marvellous pleasure. He felt, too, that he had added a cubit, or more, to his intellectual stature when Darwin's good bull-dog, Thomas Huxley, in his essay on *Man's Place in Nature*, wrote of 'the closeness of the ties' that connected man with the anthropoid apes; for he and Argo had anticipated Huxley. They — or so he claimed — had recognised their arboreal relations before Huxley ever spoke of them!

Eustace, by now, was a little unbalanced: there is no disputing that. But what I find for ever endearing about him is his continuing innocence. He never really learnt anything about himself. He was always discovering new ideas, new theories, new fragments of the scientist's knowledge, but he

never bothered to look inward and think about his own structure — except, of course, to count his responsibilities in one
chapter of his life, and measure his freedom in another. And
this splendid indifference to his own being included an almost
incredible unawareness of his physical peculiarities. For this
statement I have the evidence of his diary — a most erratic
document, now voluble, now detailed and succinct as a recipe
for tipsy cake, now empty for months at a time — for under
the date, 6 August 1869, there is this revealing note:

> Scratching myself this morning, as I got out of bed, I
> perceived (or my fingers did) what I had never noticed
> before, and that is a well-defined bony protuberance on
> the site, as far as I can judge, of the lowest of the lumbar
> vertebrae. It is about the size of a walnut: not a big one.
> Can this be the vestige of a true caudal appendage, or
> tail? Most interesting if it is. And is it a common
> phenomenon? Must enquire about this.

His enquiry, to begin with, did no harm to anyone. He
consulted his friend Argo, who immediately replied, 'Why,
yes. When I was living coldly and incongruously in a Saxon
schloss — a menial in the drawing-room and a dictator in the
schoolroom — when I was a young man trying to knock a bit
of sense into the plum-pudding heads of two high-born louts
— there was a story I heard of a family that used to live not
far away (though perhaps over the border, in Bohemia) in
which it cropped out every second generation, and always in
a female.'
'But what did, my dear Argo? What cropped out?'
'A tail, of course.'
'A true caudal appendage?'
'You could take hold of it and shake it.'
'But this is news of the first importance! Does Huxley

know of this? This will clinch everything! Where do they live — a noble family, I am sure — and what is their name?'

'It's too late to go looking for them now. They died out, it may be forty years before I ever heard of them. But they were still remembered in Saxony; and in Bohemia too, I daresay.'

Eustace was gravely disappointed, but the walnut on his rump persuaded him that somewhere there must be others, of his species, who also carried in the secrecy of modern dress a vestigial memento of their arboreal apprenticeship; and he begged Argo to ransack his memory for similar stories he might have heard while he was tutoring lumpish boys in the great houses of Europe's hinterland.

And now, I admit, I have some doubt of Argo's honesty; for he told Eustace there were many stories of that sort. In the west of Ireland, he said, the peasantry firmly believed that Protestant babies were all born with tails, and though that could be dismissed as mere prejudice, it wasn't easy to refute some of the folk-lore of Moldavia and the Pripet Marshes, or the family gossip of gaunt castles in Silesia and Ruthenia. But the trouble was that he couldn't remember any of these stories in detail, and to discover anything that would be accepted as scientific evidence would entail research. Long and patient research.

'Then come and live with me,' said Eustace. 'The tobacconists you work for can spare you, I'm sure. I have two boys — Henry is nine already, and Tom a year or so younger — and I have been meaning for some time to engage a tutor for them. I could find none better than you, I'm sure — but that would be only a morning's work for you, and the evenings would be free for research. I have a good library, and we can add to it at need. Now isn't that a capital idea?'

As it happened, it suited Argo very well, for his employers in Bristol had lately been showing some dissatisfaction with

his work. He accepted Eustace's offer at once — the wage
was generous — and within a month was teaching Henry and
Tom the rudiments of Latin grammar, and spending long,
peaceful evenings in the library with a bottle of port to assist
him in his studies.

Eustace, however, was too impatient to wait for the fruit
of Argo's research. His unfailing enthusiasm drove him to
local investigation, and within the next few months there
were many complaints, from neighbours of all degree, that
their daughters had been rudely handled and were still in a
state of nervous prostration. Owing to his position in the
county, and his great wealth, Eustace avoided most of the
penalties that a lesser man would have suffered, but more
than once, when riding after dark, he was waylaid by masked
assailants and soundly beaten.

It may be — but this I can only surmise — that he soon
found general investigation too dangerous, and thereafter
confined enquiry to his own household. For in the latter part
of this phase — it did not last very long — there are numerous
entries in his diary: *To Peg, a guinea. To Sarah in the laundry, a
guinea. To Molly in the dairy, a guinea* — and so forth. And the
inference, I think, is that Molly and Sarah and the rest of
them were glad to accept a small fee in return for a simple
demonstration that there were no vestigial tails in Somerset.
He may have satisfied himself that this was so, or he may
have tired of investigation; for he was by now in thrall to yet
another enthusiasm. This time it was architecture. He determined to rebuild his house — the old, plain Georgian house
with the added wings — and he hurried to London, not for
advice, but, as he wrote, 'to get things going at once'.

It was, I suppose, the aspiring temper of the age that
prompted the Victorian revival of the Gothic style, and to
Eustace its appeal was inescapable. He was, however, unfortunate in his choice of an architect — a young man, a

pupil of Butterfield, who appears to have found no other patron — for though he possessed great energy and abundant imagination, it may fairly be said that he lacked judgment. After only three years' work the south front of the house was nearing completion, and the façade was certainly impressive: the piers that rose between oriel windows to octagonal turrets reminded many visitors of Henry VII's Chapel in Westminster Abbey. The oriel windows themselves were very fine, but undoubtedly there were too many, and the house, as a house, had the disadvantage that it was impossible to live in it with any comfort. The statues of Old English Worthies that stood high above the central tower — in the manner of the statues above the arches of St Mark's in Venice — were also a mistake.

But the rebuilding of his house quite restored Eustace's good name in the county. With so much to watch and admire, he lost all interest in his neighbours' daughters, and no longer insulted the clergy with contemptuous remarks about the anthropoids in the Garden of Eden. It was, moreover, generally remarked that he was spending a fortune on his Gothic fancy, and it was impossible not to respect a man who had so much money 'to spare', as they said. His wife and his two sons, young as they were, showed less complacence, for they knew that his extravagance was insensate; but Emily had long lost all authority — the little show of independence that she had made as a bride had soon collapsed — and though Eustace was spending her money as well as his own, she could do nothing but gently complain to Tom and Henry of his wilfulness; and comfort herself in secret with the thought that it did at least keep him from fumbling the village girls.

When the monstrous building was completed — in its exterior parts, that is — Eustace was flattered by a message — it was really a command — from the greatest of his neighbours, the Duke of Avalon. His Grace was about to be

honoured by a visit from the Grand Duchess Anna of
Slivonia, for whose entertainment he was devising excursions
to some of the more remarkable sights in the county: the
Cheddar Gorge, the Roman remains at Bath, and Mr Vanbrugh's new house were the main items on his programme.
He told Eustace the day and hour at which they would arrive,
and added a list of some forty people whom Mrs Vanbrugh
might care to invite, and who would have the honour of
being presented to the Grand Duchess. But, he declared, the
visit would otherwise be without ceremony, and the Grand
Duchess would be attended only by her lady in waiting, the
Gräfin von Hühnewasser und Münchengrätz.

Eustace was gratified to think that his house was the object
of so much interest, but not over-awed by the grandeur of
his promised visitors. He and his architect were now busy
with the rebuilding of the stables, which, in refreshing
contrast with the great Gothic edifice, had been re-designed
after the fashion of the Gate-house at Hampton Court
Palace.

Preparation for the visit was left to Emily, who enjoyed
ten days of ceaseless activity and the agreeable deference of
her forty favoured neighbours to whom she had sent invitations. 'Let us all pray for fine weather,' she said, and though
some of them were by now inclined to accept the mechanistic
view of natural phenomena, none openly refused her request,
and the great day dawned in the serenity proper to the first
of June. Mild and clear shone the afternoon sun, and the
dust rose in a long white cloud behind the Duke of Avalon's
four-in-hand as he drove with the speed and assurance of a
famous whip through the lodge gates, and then more slowly
through the dappled shade of the mile-long avenue that led
to Eustace's Gothic monstrosity.

Eustace was not there to greet his guests. Eustace's mind
— so long closed to consideration of anything but architec-

ture — had opened a window that morning to some vague
thought or recollection of an earlier interest; and the teasing,
elusive memory had fluttered here and there, fretting itself
against the blank walls of a failing intellect like a starling that
has come down the chimney to an empty room. And then —
it was about noon — his memory settled and found a perch.
Surely Slivonia, the country of the Grand Duchess, had engaged his attention before his interest turned to architecture?
That was it! — And with a sudden excitement in his heart he
hurried off to the cottage where, for some years now, his
rascally old friend Argo had been living.

Argo had proved an excellent tutor, but since Tom and
Henry had gone to school at Sherborne his duties had been
confined to research; and Eustace had almost forgotten the
nature of the research for which he had been engaged. Nor,
for some time, had Argo wasted his energy and ingenuity on
excavating the dubious family histories of far-off barons and
distant counts from the obscurities of eastern Europe in quest
of a vestigial tail. But in the first months of his employment
he had made a *catalogue raisonnée* — how much of it was fictitious only Argo knew — of kindreds in which it was said to
recur, and of the places — the countries, provinces or villages
— where rumour of such endowment was most rife; and now
Eustace, hurrying to his cottage, was trying to recall that
tabulation of remote geography. Bessarabia was one of the
names, Wallachia another. There was a district in White
Russia, a castle near Lvov — and Slivonia! Yes, he felt sure
that Slivonia was on the list.

Argo, when he arrived, was enjoying a simple but substantial lunch of beer and bread-and-cheese and spring
onions; and Eustace invited himself to the table.

'Tell me,' he said, 'where to find that *catalogue raisonnée* you
made when we were doing our research into the matter of
the caudal appendage.'

'I thought you had forgotten about that,' said Argo with his mouth full.

'Nonsense! I never forget. And now, at this particular moment, I am most anxious to see it. Where can I find it?'

'It must be in the library,' said Argo.

'But the library, the new room, is still in total disorder.'

'Maybe I can lay my hands on it,' said Argo. 'Have some more beer.'

They finished their lunch, and returning to the house succeeded in avoiding Emily, who had been looking for Eustace but at that moment was welcoming her two sons who, having been given a day's leave from school, had just arrived. In the great new library Eustace and Argo searched unavailingly for an hour, and another hour, among stacks and piles of books, among sheaves of manuscript, in boxes, cabinets and table-drawers — and found the catalogue a few minutes before the Duke drove his four-in-hand through the lodge gates.

Eustace retired to a small upper room to study it, and Argo, who wore very smart clothes for the occasion, went off to mingle with the guests. With nervous fingers Eustace turned the pages of the catalogue, and then — yes, there it was! 'Slivonia, a Grand Duchy. In the ruling house the tradition is very old, and many of the stories appear to be well authenticated. ...'

The clatter of hooves and the brave sound of a horn alarmed him, and going to the window he looked down at the great coach, black and primrose, its doors emblazoned with the ducal arms — a little dusty now — and the four fine grey horses shaking their heads and steaming in the warm, bright air. Two grooms in top-hats and livery jumped down from the rear boot, one ran to hold the leaders, the other set steps to the box, and the Duke stood up and took off his hat to Emily who, with her guests about her, waited on the terrace. 'She looks very well!' said Eustace to himself, in some surprise — and then, more intently, quizzed the ladies who sat so high above the common earth and the well-raked gravel of his drive.

The Duchess he knew; the others, he was glad to see, were better looking. Both of them were truly handsome, and young too. Not more than twenty-eight or thirty: the one pale, dark of eye and brow, the other pink of cheek, auburn hair — blue eyes? He could not see.

Now they were getting down. Careful, a little nervous, on the steps from the box. The Duke, bulky in a great fawn coat, hat off, handing them with respectful gallantry: the Grand Duchess and the Gräfin. They were dressed — not alike, but in the same style: small bonnets, tight fitting, and tight fitting bodices; skirts with bustles. The one in dove-grey, the other lavender....

Giddy with excitement, Eustace had to leave the window and sit down. With his elbows on his knees, his head low, he felt his heart thumping. — A maid came in, running, intent on getting a good view of the great ones. She stopped, frightened, when she saw Eustace, who said, 'Bring me some brandy, I am not feeling well. But do not say I am here. Say nothing about me!' — She was a good girl, and knew her way to the butler's pantry. She was back in a few minutes with a bottle and a glass that was warm from her warm hands. She filled it generously, and kneeling, held it to his mouth. He drank, and she filled it again. He soon felt better, patted her shoulder, thanked her and told her to go. 'But leave the bottle,' he said.

He went back to the window and saw his guests scattered about the terraced garden that went downhill to the lake in great, broad steps. He could see the Grand Duchess and her lady in waiting, each with a respectful group about her — but which was which he did not know. Whom had the Duke first handed down: lavender or dove-grey? He could not remember.

Now they were walking back, and he withdrew a little, behind a curtain, lest he should be seen. There were tables on the terrace set for tea: silver glinting in the sun, white cloths, strawberries, and bric-à-brac of the pastry-cook's confectioning. His footmen in new liveries. A chorus of high voices. — He watched them in a trance of excitement that he could now control: the excitement of the hunter on his machan in the jungle waiting still and silent for the tiger to break cover. Or was it the stillness of the visionary, reading his dream in loneliness, held fast in ecstasy? — Time passed, he did not know how long, but then, in a moment of panic, he saw them rising from their tables, and feared that his visitors were going.

But no! They went down to the garden again, and turning towards the house stood to admire its window-glittering façade. Then some went farther, to the lake; there was a boat on it. One of the Slivonian ladies was apparently demanding to be taken for a row, but the other pointed to the little copse behind which the new stables were being built. She wanted to see what was going on there. And she wanted to go alone. She made gestures of refusal, very prettily, to those who offered escort, and the other lady, making a joke of it, set them all laughing. So she in dove-grey was handed into the boat, with a score of people anxious for her safety, while she in lavender went off to the stables, alone.

Now Eustace felt assured that she, the fair one in lavender, was the Grand Duchess, for had not her behaviour, her dismissal of her escorts, her noble independence, shown the perfect confidence of one born to authority? He drank a little more brandy, and had no doubt of it.

He hurried downstairs, out by a side-door, and followed her to the stables that were being built after the fashion of the Gate-house at Hampton Court Palace. They were deserted. There was no one there but the Slivonian lady in her tight-fitting lavender dress, and already she had one foot on the lowest rung of a ladder that leaned against a half-built wall.

Nervous but resolute, he walked towards her. She turned her head, and spoke to him in French. In the stress of emotion Eustace could remember no word of that language, and answered only with a bow, a worried and embarrassed smile.

She frowned — she looked enchanting when she frowned — and mustered her English. She spoke slowly but distinctly. 'You are the builder?' she asked.

'Yes,' said Eustace, 'I am the builder.'

'Good,' she said. 'You are good builder. Very clever. Much imagination.'

She climbed two or three rungs of the ladder, and rested her hands on the half-built wall. The bustle in her dress threw it out behind her like the surge of a river-wave leaping a waterfall. Eustace could see the slimness of her ankles, and his throat felt as dry as an old flour-bag.

'What will be here? In this part?' she asked.

'This is the coach-house.'

'Show me where the horses will live.'

She came down from the ladder, and they walked through an archway to the stable yard. Here she asked many questions, not all of which Eustace could answer, and again he felt his nerve failing, his excitement growing. She found a stick and scratched on the dry ground the plan of the stables as she would have designed them. She clearly knew what she was talking about, and explained exactly why her plan was preferable. Her explanation lasted a full half-hour, while Eustace, mute in admiration, watched her with ardent eyes but heard very little of what she said.

Then she exclaimed, 'Come here, and I will show you

something else,' and led him to another half-built wall, another ladder up which she climbed.

'Look here,' she said, and as she leaned forward her bustle leapt out like the bow-wave of a racing yacht. 'In here — *sacré nom de Dieu, qu'est ce que vous pouvez bien faire là-bas? Lâchez moi! Ah, que je vous y reprenne!*'

Her eyes blazing, her breast heaving, she looked down at him with vivid hatred, but Eustace, though for a moment frightened away, was desperate now, and reaching suddenly as high as he could —

'Ah, oh!' she cried. '*Au secours, au secours!*'

Down she jumped, and fell, and Eustace went with her. But now his grip was firm, there was triumph in his voice, and the strength of triumph in his hands that held her fast.

'It's true,' he shouted. 'True, true, true! She's got it, I've got it — oh, God, I wish Huxley were here! — Argo, where are you?'

Now whimpering, now screaming, now cursing him in some unknown language, now crying hoarsely '*Au secours!*', the poor dishevelled lady lay kicking on the ground, and the din of their wild duet re-echoed from the unfinished walls and beat on the nearby garden air in wave after discordant wave. The Duke and a score or so of Emily's guests were returning to the house when they heard this dire, inexplicable noise, and running to the stables, came hot-foot into the yard — then stopped, and stood aghast at what they saw.

The Duke, in the lead, magnificently kept his head. 'Go back, ma'am, go back, I beg you,' he cried. 'This is no sight for you!'

But the lady to whom he spoke paid no attention, and uttering a wilder cry than any they had heard, ran fiercely forward, broke her parasol on Eustace's bare head, and digging her nails into his cheeks, dragged him from the still fiercely kicking body of her lady in waiting.

Then, sitting on the bare ground, she pulled her untidy

friend to her lap and lavished on her such caresses, such a passionate sympathy, that all the others — all but those two were English — slowly retreated to the farthest part of the yard, lowering their eyes before a scene so embarrassing; or, at the most, looking at it sideways and as if by accident.

The Duke was visibly upset, and turned his back upon the two ladies. He had seized Eustace by the collar and marched him off as if he were a common malefactor. 'Never, never,' he exclaimed, 'did I think to see such a sight in Somerset! An Englishman, an English gentleman, who can not, at five o'clock in the afternoon, restrain his passion or bridle the beast in him!'

But Eustace, though his face was bleeding, was strangely unperturbed. Oh, better than that! As Argo reported it — Argo had arrived in time to see it all —

He was just seraphic, bar the blood on his cheeks. Never have I seen him so happy, and to very few can it have been vouchsafed to see on any human face that look of mild, benignant, total satisfaction. When the Duke reproved him for his unbridled passion, he laughed outright and said, 'The passion of the scientist is the mind's purity in a blaze of enlightenment! There is nothing guilty, nothing unworthy, nor ever has been, in any act or emotion of mine since the days of my boyhood.'

At this the Duke was fairly flabbergasted. The complacency of the man took his breath away. And when Mr Vanbrugh went on to say, 'I hope to persuade the Grand Duchess to let me publish my findings; or, at the least, to write and tell Mr Huxley' — well, then he got a little nervous, for clearly he thought Mr Vanbrugh was clean out of his mind.

But at that moment the two ladies, who had recovered a little of their composure and tidied themselves up, came walking very slowly towards us, and the odd thing was that the Grand Duchess, whose complexion had been dead white, was now as red as a tomato, and the Gräfin, who had looked fine and rosy, was as pale as the undersides of a flounder. The Grand Duchess was the one in grey, not, as Mr Vanbrugh had supposed, the one in lavender: she was the Gräfin. And when they came near, they both stopped, and the Grand Duchess spat in Mr Vanbrugh's face. 'You pig!' she said. 'You English pig!'

But Mr. Vanbrugh just smiled, still pleased and happy, and said, 'I assure you, madam, that I have done the Grand Duchess no harm — '

'Of course you have done the Grand Duchess no harm! I am the Grand Duchess, and I would not have let you come near me. Neither you nor any man.'

Then Mr Vanbrugh looked very disconcerted. '*You* are the Grand Duchess?' he asked. 'Then who, may I ask, is this lady?'

'Are you a fool as well as a pig? She is my lady in waiting, the Gräfin von Hühnewasser und Münchengrätz.'

'But I thought it was in *your* family that the vestige recurred!' — Poor Mr Vanbrugh was now very puzzled indeed; and then a happy thought struck him, and leaning forward he whispered, '*Have you got a tail too?*'

At that the Gräfin went into hysterics, the Grand Duchess struck Mr Vanbrugh in the face with both her fists at once — just like two hammers — and the Duke, God bless him, showed the moral greatness of the English aristocracy by hooking them on his two arms, one on either side, and walking them off, to my great relief. All the rest followed but me and Mr Vanbrugh — and the Gräfin's bonnet, that still lay in the dust. He made nothing of the beating he had got, but said to me, very earnestly, 'Now this is most important, Argo, and if in fact she has one, it may mean that the incidence in Slivonia is far commoner than anyone has yet suspected!'

But then I explained things to him, for in the garden I had had a long talk with the Duchess — not the Grand Duchess, but Her Grace of Avalon — and I had learnt the story of the Gräfin's unhappy marriage. Her parents had forced her into it, and it lasted less than a month. The Grand Duchess had always been against it, and when the Gräfin wrote and said her husband was a brute, she replied at once, *Come back to Slivonia and be my lady in waiting.* They had been the closest of friends since childhood, you see; for they're full cousins.

Mr Vanbrugh thought awhile about that, and then said, 'Now I understand why the Grand Duchess was so upset. She was just like a mother to the Gräfin, wasn't she? The way she took her on her lap and kissed her: just like a mother with a child who's fallen and hurt her knee.'

And then, a little later, he said more cheerfully, 'But if they're first cousins *It's still in the family* — and that, after all, is what we wanted to know, isn't it? I think we've proved our case, Argo, and I'm pretty sure I ought to write to Huxley about it.'

But I told him no. I told him Mr Huxley would need more data....

This long extract, in Argo's handwriting, I found among the family papers. It was part of a letter that he had begun to write — to an old friend in America with whom he maintained correspondence — but he never finished it, nor posted it, because one of the boys, either Tom or Harry, found and purloined it. They, inevitably, were both miserably ashamed and bitterly embarrassed by all that had happened, and for a week or two stayed sulkily at home, refusing to go back to school under such a weight of unhappiness.

But there was no public scandal. In the county, of course, it gave conversation till Christmas — there had been no such ripeness of gossip since the time of the second Duchess of Avalon, and our family was the cause of that too — but except for a little leakage here and there, it was kept within the county. The Grand Duchess and her lady in waiting went home rather sooner than they had intended, and no more was heard from them. Neither of them married, but they may have lived happily enough for all that. No one remembers them now, nor even their Duchy; which vanished from the maps after the first Great War.

Eustace, I think, was fairly happy in the last six months of his life. He had his monstrous house, he had (to his own satisfaction) established evolution as, if not a visible, at least a palpable fact, and he lived to see his new stables very handsomely completed. That was a stormy winter, however, and the new house suffered a good deal of damage in great gales from the south-west. One of the English Worthies was blown from the top of the central tower on a wild night when Eustace, who had a Gothic passion for tempestuous weather, was walking on the terrace. It went through the roof, and sent down a scattering of slates; one of which struck him on the side of the head.

He recovered consciousness, but no one expected him to live, nor did he. Emily and the two boys were with him at the end, and a little while before he died he spoke quite clearly to them, and smiled in a curious, complacent, self-satisfied way.

'You think I'm an old booby,' he said. 'Oh, yes, you do! I know what goes on in the house, there's very little that escapes me. *That old booby* is what you say about me, but you don't know the half of it. No one becomes a booby without good reason, and what I say is, You should have known my father! Now he *was* a booby!'

v Reform – and Then What?

THE midshipmen's berth in the frigate *Impérieuse*, 38
guns, smelt strongly of cheese. There were, indeed,
many other essences and odours, of tarpaulin jackets, of wet
hemp from the cable-tier, a rank and healthy exhalation of
onions, a draught of malt and hops, the almost feral *bouquet*
of young, male humanity — but the concert of perfumes was
dominated by cheese, and for this the purser was to blame;
his issue-room was separated from the midshipmen's mess-
place only by a canvas screen, and he having lost his nose
(in a very gallant action off the coast of Spain) had had no
compunction in buying several hundredweights of mouldy
Cheshire at a price which greatly fortified his claim to be a
strict economist.

Despite its sullen perfumes, the mess-place was clean and
well tended. The canvas screens that enclosed it were

scrubbed white, and the deck had been holystoned so hard and often that its planking looked like a fine table-cloth. Nor were the young men who occupied the berth at odds with the decency of their surroundings, for the *Impérieuse* had only lately left Plymouth, and hardly one of them had not put on clean linen ten days before. To a landsman their quarters would have looked a little crowded, but that could not be avoided when a ship whose gun-deck was barely a hundred and fifty feet long had to find accommodation for just over three hundred men; and the midshipmen, the mates, the assistant surgeons and the clerks who messed together in a canvased square of the cockpit and slung their hammocks, haunch to haunch, in the cable-tier, managed their affairs in what seemed to them a tolerable comfort.

They were now in a relaxed and easy mood, drinking flip and inclined for mischief. The ship lay at anchor in the Basque Roads, and not far away, in the straits east of the Isle d'Oléron and off the misty, low-lying French mainland between Rochefort and La Rochelle, was a fleet of fifteen sail, the destruction of which was the pressing and particular duty of their captain, Lord Cochrane. But the midshipmen and their companions showed no concern for the future, no interest in the battle, or preparations for battle, that might be ordered as soon as Cochrane returned from the flagship. They were happily intent on the medical treatment — for a sore throat — that had been prescribed for a midshipman called Jeremy (or more commonly Jem) Vanbrugh.

Jem Vanbrugh was in his fifteenth year, and had served at sea since he was eleven. He had been in the frigate *Pallas* when Cochrane destroyed three French corvettes in the impossible waters of the Garonne — in the fight against the frigate *Minerve*, among the shoals where they now lay — with Cochrane in the Mediterranean when His Lordship fought, as it seemed, with one foot on land, the other in the sea, and harassed an army in the intervals between capturing the ships on which it depended. He had served under his intrepid Captain in Fort Trinidad, when for twelve wild days a few sailors and marines withstood the French assault on Rosas. That was just seven months before, in September, 1808. – And now, on the threshold of another battle, but before crossing the threshold, he was going to be laughed at, made game of, and bullied by a few boys of his own age and some young men who were not much older.

Jem Vanbrugh was a boy with a placid temperament and very little imagination. He never failed in a given duty, but rarely showed any initiative. He once took a boat in under the guns of a Spanish fort to cut out a xebec, and would certainly have been successful had he been less punctilious; but he waited for the lieutenant in command of the foray to slip the cable of his larger prize and lead the way out – and was sunk at anchor. On another occasion, under fire that killed or disabled all the crew of a carronade, he and one able seaman, both lightly wounded had served it till the action was broken off; and when commended for his resolution he had looked extremely puzzled and explained, 'But no one told me to stop firing.'

On such occasions, when under orders, he seemed quite fearless; but not because he did not know the meaning of fear. An order, to him, was something inescapable, and often he showed great valiancy in doing his duty because he could not think of doing anything else. But in private circumstances, with nothing but his own wits to instruct him, he was sometimes bewildered and humiliated by boys who were a little cleverer than himself – some of whom, it is likely, resented his habitual courage in action – and because, in youth, his appearance was only a trifle short of being ludicrous, there were seasons when he had to endure a lot of bullying.

He wore habitually a look of vacant innocence, and his hair, which was dark and thick, grew low on his forehead. He had good, wide-open eyes, a delicate mouth and chin; but his ears were enormous and stood out like a bat's. He was forever being told to clew up and haul them down, that it was no weather for stu'nsails — and he had learnt to ignore these dull, professional jokes. But to some of the rougher sort there was a recurrent temptation to seize and pull and twist such remarkable features — indeed, they seemed to invite it — and though Jem had fought a dozen times for the honour of his ears, he had not then learnt to use his fists in a scientific way and he was always beaten; which he found discouraging.

And now, when he was suffering from a sore throat, his tormentors found a new approach, and loudly applauded the young assistant surgeon who told him to open his mouth.

The senior midshipman, a heavily built, ginger-haired, loutish young Scot called Hay — whose father had some influence with Cochrane — was their ringleader, and he held Jem's hands behind his back while the assistant surgeon thrust a paint-brush loaded with a dark and viscous fluid into his mouth and briskly swabbed his inflamed throat and tonsils. Jem choked and retched, the young surgeon took him by the hair to hold him still, and Hay declared, 'Don't spoil the ship for a ha'porth of tar, he'll need three coats at least.'

About this time, in the flagship of Admiral Lord Gambier, who commanded the Channel Fleet that was blockading the fifteen French ships of war in the Aix Roads between Oléron and the mainland, there was a display of ill-temper that made the noisy ragging in the cockpit of the *Impérieuse* look, in comparison, mild and innocuous. Briefly the situation was that Lord Gambier did not want to engage the Frenchmen;

that Cochrane had been sent by the First Lord of the
Admiralty to destroy them; and that Rear-Admiral Harvey,
third in command of the Channel Fleet, deeply resented
Cochrane's arrival because he wanted to command the
operation himself.

Gambier, Harvey and Cochrane were all important
figures. Gambier had a rich wife, influential relations, and
had claimed kinship with Pitt. Harvey was wealthy in his
own right, he had commanded the *Téméraire* at Trafalgar,
and was connected by marriage with the Prime Minister.
Cochrane was the poor heir to a poor Scotch earldom — poor
save for the prize-money he had won — but he was generally
thought of as the most brilliant naval commander since
Nelson. — And give Gambier the credit for prudence at
least: the French ships, among the off-shore shoals, lay within
a huge, triangular boom, and to attack them would be
perilous indeed. A dozen fire-ships had been commissioned,
but could fire-ships break the heavy boom? 'The attempt is
hazardous, if not desperate,' said Gambier, and offered Cochrane no help whatever — except in the matter of tracts. He
was an ardent Methodist, and a firm believer in tracts. If
Cochrane had not enough for his ship's company, Gambier
could let him have plenty, and be very glad to.

Then, in the Captain's cabin — its great windows opened
immediately above the wide stern-gallery of the Admiral's
quarters — Cochrane continued the conversation with Harvey, and Harvey, empurpled with anger, strode noisily to and
fro, and bellowed, 'I'm no canting Methodist! I'm no hypo-
crite, I'm no psalm-singer!' — He could not control his
contempt for Gambier. — 'If Lord Nelson were here, he
wouldn't have anchored at all! He'd have gone straight at
the Frenchmen,' he shouted, 'as I was ready to go, as soon as
the fire-ships fetched up! Here's a list of officers — *my*
officers! — whom I've advised of the operation, and told

them, God damn it, that I would lead them. And now, God damn it, you have come to steal the glory from us!'

Cochrane replied that he had received his orders from the First Lord in person, and could do no more than obey them; and Harvey, in a new access of temper, stamped on the deck — the resounding deck above Gambier's cabin — and declared, 'This isn't the first time I've been lightly treated! It isn't the first time my services have been overlooked — and all because I'm no canting Methodist!' Furiously he stamped to the open windows — open above the windows below — and with a rancorous thought in his mind of the rich and elderly heiress whom Gambier had married, shouted, 'But this I can say for myself, that I'm not one of those who cheat old women out of their estates!'

In the cockpit of the *Impérieuse* — in the midshipmen's berth enclosed by white-scrubbed canvas — the bullying of Jem Vanbrugh had gone a little farther. After the inside of his throat had been well painted, it had occurred to Hay that as the medicine was dark brown, sticky, and evil-smelling, it would be good for Jem to have his neck daubed with it, and a bandage applied. The bandage gave him a stiff and vertical look, and inspired in Hay a new idea. There was a set of darts in the mess-room, that the ship's blacksmith had made, and Jem's head on its immobile column would make a better target than the coloured canvas at which they commonly threw. So Jem was set against a bulkhead, and told to stand still. 'And I,' said Hay, 'will make a pattern round your head as close as an old woman's mutch.'

The first two darts stuck quivering in the wood an inch or so on either side of Jem's temples. The third drew a shout of delight from the spectators — for it was aimed at a point an inch above the centre line of Jem's head, but flew so low that its feathers were lost to sight in the thickness of his hair —

and the fourth drew a howl of pain from Jem's own lips, for it pierced the open wing of his right ear and pinned him to the bulkhead. At this hilarious mishap everyone in the mess-room hallooed and shouted with laughter — some almost collapsed in their merriment — and poor Jem might have stood there in his pain (a minor Sebastian) till they had exhausted their pleasure, had it not been for an opportune shrill sound from the deck above.

Captain Cochrane had returned from the flagship, and the boatswain's mates were piping him aboard. To Jem it seemed the sweetest music he had ever heard, and the others it immediately recalled to seemliness and duty. Some ran up the cockpit ladder, others forward to tasks they had forgotten, and Hay had the goodness not only to unpin his victim from the bulkhead, but to give him a can of flip; which, through the paint that bedaubed his throat, tasted unlike any flip he had ever drunk before.

Cochrane's plan to breach the great boom, within which the French fleet lay, was to send against it what in effect were enormous floating mines, that he himself had designed. There were two of them, small vessels in which, on a floor of stout logs, fifteen hundred barrels of gunpowder were packed into puncheons lashed together, built into a mass with wet sand, and topped with a load of fused shells and hand grenades.

Choosing a lieutenant and four seamen for his crew, Cochrane led the assault in the bigger of his mine-ships. The fire-ships had orders to follow through the breaches in the boom, but the night was dark and moonless, the sea ran high, the wind blew hard. Few of the fire-ships found their way, and most of them were set alight and abandoned too soon. Cochrane's own vessel rammed the boom, the fuses were lighted, a gig was launched, and he and his crew rowed away. In that wild sea they had not gone far when a huge explosion rocked the sky and for a few pulse-beats reddened the dark, swagging clouds and the white-rimmed waves. The wreckage fell beyond them — they were still so near the boom — and great spars plunged into the crested waves to windward.

With three other frigates the *Impérieuse*, plunging to her anchors, lay off a nearby shoal. She was waiting for the crews of the fire-ships — homing in their small boats — and one of them, that had gone astray in the wild darkness of the night, came riding down on the smaller of the mine-ships that was still made fast astern of the *Impérieuse*. She fouled the cables that bound them, and for a few minutes lay grinding and crashing, now against the one, now the other; and rubbed their sides with imminent menace. But a man — or a boy — snatching an axe, ran to the bitts and cutting the tow-ropes set the mine-ship adrift. Both it and the fire-ship disappeared in the darkness to leeward, and aboard the *Impérieuse* a conscientious officer took note of him whose quick wit and the speed of his action had freed her from danger. He was Jem Vanbrugh.

Two days later, with a glass of wine and a biscuit on the table before him, and somewhat ill at ease, he sat in the Captain's cabin while Cochrane re-read the report he had newly written of an action which had been less successful than it deserved. Also with them was an elderly lieutenant in command of a gun-brig that had arrived, an hour or two before, with despatches from England.

Cochrane's assault had started a panic in the French fleet. In ship after ship the anchor cables were cut, and they drifted ashore. In the morning all but two were on the beach. Three or four were engaged at close range, by the frigates that Cochrane led, and burnt. But Gambier in his flagship still cruised far out to sea, and nothing would persuade him to come closer. — The French ships re-floated on the rising tide, there were batteries on the little island of Aix and the larger island of Oléron, and the shoals were dangerous. Gambier preferred sea-room and his tracts. — So Cochrane had written his despatch without much commendation for the Admiral.

He signed and sanded it, passed the bottle to the old lieutenant, and turned to Jem with an expression in which, for a moment, there was a sort of curiosity, as if he had never seen him before; but then he frowned, with worry or vexation, and exclaimed abruptly, 'I have sad news for you.'

He paused, and picked up a little knife — trimmed his pen — and setting off on a new tack, said, 'You acted in a prompt and seamanlike way when the fire-ship bore down on us. You have done well throughout, on the Spanish coast very well, but the matter of clearing the fire-ship, that was more than I had looked for in you. — Or did someone tell you to take an axe, and cut her loose?'

Jem, head down, stared at the deck — twiddled his hat — and muttered no, he had heard no order. There was so much noise, it had been difficult to hear anything, he said.

'Then,' said Cochrane, 'I would have recommended you for your action. I would have had it brought to the notice of the Lord Commissioners — if, that is, you had been staying with us in the naval service. But it would do you no good now that you are leaving us.'

At that, Jem looked up with consternation on his face, and in his mind a frightened search for recent faults, for some misdeed so grave that he must be dismissed his ship — dismissed, perhaps with ignominy, from the navy — for that, it seemed, was what Cochrane threatened. But the Captain was off on another tack.

'I have never met your father,' he said. 'It was a Mr Dabney from Dorset — your uncle, I think — who came to speak for you. That was three years ago, and since then — you haven't seen your father since then, have you?'

'It's very seldom that I ever saw him,' said Jem. 'He had no interest in his children, and now, I think, we could pass each other on a busy street, and neither recognise the other.'

'So if you were told ill news of him, you would hear it bravely?'

'Is he dead?'

'He is.'

'He was pretty old, of course,' said Jem.

'Old! Old?' exclaimed Cochrane. 'Here in these papers that have come, it says he was just six-and-thirty. D'you call that old? God help you to understanding, it's barely two years older than I myself am.'

Sadly the grey-haired lieutenant from the gun-brig shook his head, and filled his glass again. Cochrane, angry for a moment, stared at Jem — then laughed aloud — and said, 'Well, it would save a deal of grief if we all admitted that our fathers owe God a death. You may have the making of a philosopher in you, and that should help you in your new condition of life. You are your father's heir — do you understand that? And I have orders for England again, so we'll put you ashore at Plymouth, and that's the last you'll ever see of the King's navy.'

Jem made his bow, and left them; and when he had gone Cochrane said to the lieutenant, 'Did you ever see an estate of £8,000 a year?'

'It's not the sort of landfall a sailor looks for,' said the old man.

'You have just seen it go out on the back of that young gentleman with the big ears.'

'A midshipman worth £8,000 a year? God spare us such a thought!'

'God spare us indeed. It would be the ruination of the service. But he'll go home and find ruin of his own. He's not the boy to carry weight of that sort.'

Five years later Lord Cochrane, then a Member of Parliament for Westminster, was found guilty of fraudulent stock-jobbing and sentenced to a year's imprisonment. Whether he was guilty or not is a matter of opinion. On February 12th, 1814, he bought, on a margin, government stock to the tune of £139,000. A week later a Frenchman called de Berenger arrived in England with the story that Bonaparte had been killed. The funds went up, and on the 20th, before de Berenger's story was disproved, Cochrane sold out and made a handsome profit. He was expelled from Parliament, but his constituents of Westminster, passionately asserting his innocence, promptly re-elected him. By then, however, he was in the Marshalsea — where, as fellow-prisoners, he found three old shipmates. Two of them were seamen who, after their sound training in the *Pallas* and *Impérieuse*, had taken — but unsuccessfully — to piracy; and the third was Jem Vanbrugh, who had been committed for a debt of £3,450. The seamen were hanged, and Cochrane lived to give much of South America most of its freedom from Spain and Portugal. To Jem Vanbrugh fortune was less dramatic in her awards, but he made a modest name for himself — and died in a frantic endeavour to save the life of his old commander.

Neither Cochrane nor anyone else who knew him well was surprised to hear of him in the Marshalsea. From the midshipman's berth in a hard-fighting frigate — by way of a fortune of £8,000 a year — he had laid a direct course for it, and the only circumstance of unusual interest in his passage was that his pilot was his old enemy, the loutish young Scot called Hay.

For two or three years his mother had kept Jem at home, engaged tutors for him, and done what she could to mend his manners and give him a gentleman's education. They lived a secluded life, for his father's sudden death, in very peculiar circumstances, had started a great scandal in Somerset, and

Mrs Vanbrugh was much affected by the unkind gossip. Properly used, this time of retirement should have given lasting benefits to Jem; but it gave him nothing. For education he showed no aptitude whatever, and when his mother began to take him and his sister to Bath, to become acquainted with polite society, he deserted them as soon as he could and took his pleasure drinking with grooms and stable-boys. It was in Bath, however, that he was shown the way to a dissolute enlargement of his life — and then, for a while, to the confinement of prison.

He was walking one day, at great speed, from the Pump Room — where, with some meagre excuse, he had left his mother and sister — when he heard behind him a voice that was in part familiar, but in other parts overlaid by a strange, fashionable accent.

'What's the hurry, Vanbrugh? In God's name, what's the hurry? You're like a fifth-rater coming into the chops of the Channel with a full westerly behind her — stu'nsails set and a bone in her teeth — but her sticks won't stand the strain! Not with all that canvas set. Those ears, by God! I'd know them in a dark night, from the Nore to the Gulf of Rosas!'

The young man who had shouted, and brought him to a halt, delivered the rest of his harangue with great animation — flourishing his cane to the danger of passers-by — and under the disguise of an affected voice, and clothes in the height of fashion, Jem, with some reluctance, recognised his former shipmate Hay.

It was this encounter that set the course of Jem's life. In spite of his smart clothes and air of dashing assurance, Hay, in Bath, was a lonely young man, and very glad to meet someone to whom he could talk easily and boast with due effect. He and Jem spent the rest of the day together — Hay had discovered a taste for wine, he now called flip 'a drench for poor tarpaulins' — and after two or three bottles they forgot the scorn or hatred they had once felt for each other, and remembered only the glorious fact that they had shared the hardships and danger of sea-service under the dauntless Cochrane. It was Hay who insisted that this made them immeasurably superior to the idle world in which they were now living, and though Jem found this hard to believe — for the loud, bright voices and the fashionable airs of Bath oppressed him heavily — he was vaguely comforted by it. It was he who called for the next bottle.

To begin with, Hay said he had left the navy when an uncle died and bequeathed him an estate in Perthshire; but after the third bottle he told the truth, which was that his uncle, so far from dying, had married again, for the fourth time — and he, almost simultaneously, had found a chance of escaping from the sea when the widow of a ship-chandler in Plymouth insisted on giving him her late husband's gold watch and chain. They had married, and she made him very comfortable. But she was old enough to be his mother, and now she had begun to show a motherly disapproval of his extravagance. Which was doubly absurd, for it was she who had first encouraged him to wear good clothes and cut a fine figure in the world.

Until then it had not occurred to Jem that he too was being hardly treated. Since his father's death, one of his mother's several brothers had lived with them, to manage the estate — this was the 'Mr Dabney from Dorset' who first recommended him to Cochrane — and from him Jem received a modest allowance. It had been sufficient for his needs, but now he compared it with the large figures of his whole income, and found he had been used with gross injustice. He asked Hay for an opinion — told Hay what he was worth — and in stark amazement Hay fell flat on his back with a broken chair beneath him.

He picked himself up and shouted to a waiter for another

bottle. '£8,000 a year,' he exclaimed, 'and all he gives you is a parson's living! By God, it's bloody robbery, it's piracy on the highways of England, the Dey of Algiers is a sucking innocent beside him! But I'll save you, Jem, I'll come in under his guns for you if it's the last good act of my life. I'll cut you out, and we'll cruise together, like free men! We'll set a course for London. We'll show our colours in St James's. We'll board the Cyprians, and take the gaming-hells by storm. We'll scatter the Charleys, we'll teach 'em to cut and run when they see the topsails of the old *Impérieuse* in the straits of Drury Lane! Another bottle, Jem, and forty thousand more to follow!'

Both were carried home, dead drunk, and confusion ensued when the chairmen delivered Hay to Mrs Vanbrugh's lodgings, Jem to the widow of the ship-chandler. But in the general surliness of the following day the mood of rebellion was established, and a few weeks later they were living together, in rooms not far from the Post Office in St Martin's-le-Grand (where the mail-coaches stopped) on the promise of a very comfortable income. Under great pressure — in some fear, indeed, of physical assault, for Hay had become truculent in his demand for justice — Mr Dabney of Dorset had agreed to pay Jem an allowance of £1,200 a year: to which Hay, with becoming modesty, offered another £600 — the annuity, he declared, that his wife had settled on him unconditionally.

In spite of freedom, however, and a joint income of a little more than £1,200 — Hay's 'annuity' was fictitious, and the ship-chandler's widow was disinclined to support a husband *in absentia* — they lived for some time in a subdued and modest style, for London frightened them. Its crowded streets, the din and clatter of its traffic, the great gardened countryside of the parks, the cavalcade of fashion in the Row, the elegant new architecture of a Bloomsbury square — the cadgers, ruffians, pimps and broken-down whores in a gin-shop, sluicing their ivories with blue ruin, or a demented crowd at Newgate waiting for the drop of a paper-faced murderer — such things as these over-awed them and reduced their spirits. Within a week or two of coming to town they had seen the Prince Regent — they had stopped to stare at Brummel framed in the big window at White's — and they had been caught and held fast in the huge, stinking crowd that watched the hanging of John Bellingham; who, a few days before, had shot Mr Spencer Perceval, Chancellor of the Exchequer, in the lobby of the House of Commons. Before such scenes they realised their youth and inexperience; and trod the pavements warily. But not for long.

Cold ham and rack-punch (too much rack-punch) at Vauxhall introduced them to a Mr Springer, who had a horse to sell. Mr Springer took them to Tattersall's — later introduced them to his tailor and his bootmaker — found them lodgings in a better part of the town, not half a mile from Bond Street — rode with them in the Park, and added his own bill for corn and stabling to theirs. Now they felt more at home, and £1,200 a year (the ship-chandler's widow still contributed very little) was barely enough to support them. But Mr Springer knew ways and means of raising money — easy enough for a young gentleman with an estate on his back — and for those in the know, he said, there was money to be picked up, like strawberries in their season, on any one of several nearby racecourses. Mr Springer took them racing.

Three times in the next two years Jem's Uncle Dabney paid his debts, and then, after long and anxious consultation with his mother, wrote to say that in future he could look for no more help, but if he exceeded his allowance must take the consequences. By this time Mr Springer had disappeared from their knowledge — he was indiscriminate in love, and his health had suffered — but Jem and his constant friend

Hay had learnt, as they thought, enough about life to look after themselves, and neither believed that Uncle Dabney's threat had any substance in it. The whole estate was Jem's, by inheritance, and who could keep it from him? — But Jem had quite forgotten that when he first came home from sea he had signed a paper, at his mother's insistence, by which he appointed her and Uncle Dabney his guardians and administrators of the estate until he was twenty-one. He had no cause to remember it, for he had not read it.

In 1814, then — the year of Lord Cochrane's disgrace — he was committed to the Marshalsea with debts of £3,450, for much of which Hay was responsible. Jem went to prison and Hay suffered almost as deeply, for with no other means of support he had to go home to Plymouth and seek forgiveness from the ship-chandler's widow. But though he had not been faithful to her, he was still faithful to Jem, and six months later, when Mrs Vanbrugh and Uncle Dabney relented and paid their debts, Hay was back in London, with £50 that the widow (doting again) had given him, to welcome Jem on his release.

That winter there was, in London, a fog of inordinate density and memorable duration — and after the fog a Siberian air that froze, not only every pool and stream in the south of England, but the great river itself: froze it to such a depth that the Thames became a fair-ground, and while all its traffic was held in arctic stability — there were forty ships in the ice between Wapping and the Isle of Dogs — high carnival reigned from London Bridge to Chelsea, and at night the Cockneys danced between the bonfires that glittered on its stilled and echoing pavement.

On the first night of the fog, when Jem, not long out of the Marshalsea, was still in a mood to celebrate his freedom, he and his friend fell into a scrape that might have sent them both to prison. Their evening began at Covent Garden, but

128

they saw nothing of the play, for they got no farther than the saloon. There they drank a good deal, talked nonsense with women of the town, whom they called Cyprians or Lady-birds — bought them a glass of wine or a dish of jelly, but refused their invitations, for their minds were on more robust amusement — they listened, with nudge and wink, to the ridiculous conversation of old, decayed gentlemen of fashion, and quarrelled mildly with younger gentlemen, or those who aspired to be thought gentlemen — they accepted a card from a girl whose attendant bawd was keeping a sharp eye on her lest she brush off and pawn the new dress she was wearing — Hay pulled the nose of an inoffensive person who, he declared, was the cove who kept a case where he had lately had his pocket picked — and when the lights went out they sought a familiar gin shop where the company was rougher and a quartern of Old Tom was the usual consolation for those who had no beds to go to.

An hour or two there, then a cup of coffee and a toasted muffin to restore their senses — and in the shadow of an archway, hardly visible in the growing fog, they found an old Charley asleep in his box. Quickly they had him down, with a crash and a wakening shout, and stood there laughing, crowing in triumph, while the old man's heels kicked against the echoing box and hoarsely he screamed for help.

Then Hay, who thought he heard a distant rattle, exclaimed, 'Now let's be off!'

'We must turn him over first, and let him out,' said Jem and stooped to the box; in which, indeed, the old man could do nothing to help himself.

'There's no time for that,' said Hay, and ran.

Across the street another old Charley woke and sprang his rattle. Jem saw his lantern glowing yellow in the fog — heard a shout, 'Watch, Watch!' — more rattles, more lanterns — and being a little fuddled, ran this way first, then

turned and ran the other. Someone hit him on the head
with a heavy stick, another hit him on the back — but now
he had learnt to use his fists, and punching hard he dropped
them both and bolted into the cover of the fog.

In the morning he quarrelled bitterly with Hay, accusing
him of desertion in face of the enemy — Hay countered with
a charge of rank sentiment and folly — for who but a soft-
hearted fool would risk being lugged off to the Watch House,
then to Bow Street, for the sake of comforting an old Charley?

The quarrel continued for some days, till they decided to
have it out, with mufflers on, in Gentleman Jackson's rooms.
— Both had taken instruction there, but Jem, because at first
he knew less of the art than Hay, had been more assiduous in
practice, and now thought himself the better boxer. — Jackson was agreeable, promised to find seconds, and himself to
referee the match. — They went the next day, and because
the weather was now so cold that sparrows were dropping
dead on the wing the rooms at 13 Bond Street were empty but
for Jackson and the seconds, and two youngish (but not
young) gentlemen whom Jem recognised as the sort known as
'bang-up Corinthians'. One was Mr Brook, the other Mr
Hart. When Jem and Hay had stripped, Mr Brook offered
to wager £50 on Jem, and as Mr Hart liked the look of Hay
the bet was made.

The fight was short and vigorous. It began with Jem
going down to a cross-buttock, and in the second round being
floored by a tremendous right-hander. But he needed
punishment to make him work, and in the next three rounds
Hay's body was patterned with bruises like a thrush's breast,
his right eye was closed, and his nose became a fountain. In
the seventh round he was clouted twice on the mark — being
somewhat out of condition, these punches hurt him — and
when Jem closed his other eye with a straight left, Jackson
declared he had had enough, and Jem was the winner. Mr

Brook and Mr Hart were well pleased with the exhibition, and resumed the conversation it had interrupted.

This had to do with a proposal to race their tandem-drawn Stanhope gigs on the frozen Serpentine. They were both famous whips, now equally enamoured of the chance to drive against each other in conditions that would make the management of horses in tandem even more difficult than usual — and perhaps impossible. Each was prepared to bet £500 that he could overcome both difficulties and his rival, and Gentleman Jackson had agreed to be the judge. They had just arranged to meet at noon the next day when Jem and Hay, having washed and dressed, returned to be congratulated once more on their display, and to drink a glass or two of brandy and water.

It occurred to Mr Brook that the race on the ice would be more interesting if he and Mr Hart carried a passenger. — 'The more weight the better,' said Mr Hart. 'It'll give us a firmer grip.' — 'I suppose we can't ask a lady?' said Mr Brook. — 'No, no, wouldn't do at all. Break their legs, offend their mamas, cold looks at Almack's: couldn't face it.' — 'Then these young gladiators: let us take them!' — 'A very good notion. Mr Vanbrugh, Mr Hay, will you join us on the Serpentine to-morrow?'

They found, the next day, a great crowd waiting in the Park, for news of the wager had quickly gone round. A silver-gilt sun shone brightly on the snow, and above and about the people on the banks of the lake their frozen breath hung like a thin cloud in the still, arctic air. The race was to start from the bridge — round the island — and back to the bridge if they survived. But the odds against both returning were ten to one, and the knowing men muttered sagely, 'If you want to break your neck, go in a tandem.'

Mr Brook's gig was black with yellow wheels, and he drove a pair of greys; Mr Hart's were bay mares, his gig was yellow with red wheels. They stood together on the south bank of the Serpentine, the horses well blanketed, with grooms at their head. The swells, the Corinthians, gathered round them to watch a couple of farriers roughing the horses' shoes, and offer or take fantastic bets — and Jem and Hay, now feeling a little nervous, a little cold in spite of their heavy driving-coats, waited with uneasy patience and expressions of bleak indifference.

At noon exactly the rugs were taken from the horses, and their grooms led them to the starting-place by the bridge. Between the gloved fingers of his left hand Mr Brook felt the ordered reins: near-leading between forefinger and thumb, the off-leading and the near-wheeling between forefinger and middle finger, the off-wheeling at the bottom next the third finger — and Mr Hart did the same, then took his whip from its socket — and so did Mr Brook. The grooms retired, and Mr Brook and Mr Hart delicately shortened their reins — feeling the mouth of the wheeler, holding the leader back a little — then Gentleman Jackson cried, 'If you are ready, gentlemen?' — and fired a pistol into the air.

With a hollow tumult of drumming hooves and a roar of wheels they were off. Suddenly the air was a frozen razor on their chins — but for a little while at least they were in no great danger, for on that part of the lake there was a light carpet of frozen snow that roughened the surface and gave the wheels a grip. Like iron upon iron was the roaring of the wheels, the near yellow of Mr Brook (who was on the right) within a foot of Mr Hart's red, and the leaders running nose to nose. The wind of their passage brought the blood to their cheeks, tears to their eyes, and distantly to their ears came the cheering of the crowd. Matched in speed and matched by skill, the horses stretched to the race their satin-smooth shoulders, muscle-filled rumps, and made of their symmetry a beauty that was potent and purposive.

But now, ahead of them, both drivers saw danger. Between the island and the north bank of the lake the ice was black and smooth, for the wind that brought the snow had blown from the south-east — the island had sheltered the narrow strait — and cunningly, strongly, Mr Brook with his whip-hand shortened his reins, checked leader and wheeler with the same firm pressure — so did Mr Hart — and still wheel to wheel and nose to nose they passed through the strait at a steady trot, then gently turned to double the island. But not slowly enough.

For now, turning on the mirror-smooth ice, Mr Brook's yellow wheels went sliding to the left, to the imminent peril of Mr Hart, who loudly shouted 'Damnation!', touched his leader with the whip to pull out of danger — but his leader, in spite of rasped hooves, went down on her tail and slid like a toboggan — the wheeler reared and fell, broke a shaft and broke a trace — and Mr Hart and his passenger were tumbled out upon the ice.

But Mr Brook was no better off, for when his leading grey felt the sideways pull of the wheels he suddenly turned right-about and faced his driver in great alarm and indignation. He reared — the wheeler reared to meet him, and for a moment they stood facing each other as if under tuition in the Viennese *haute école* — then both fell, one on either side — shafts broke, traces broke, Mr Brook and his passenger fell out, and the one skinned his knees, the other his nose, on the ice.

The match was called off and all bets were cancelled except those that had offered ten to one that no one would finish. The grooms came running up with blankets, covered the trembling horses and led them off, the crowd stopped laughing and gave three hearty cheers, and Mr Brook and Mr Hart took their passengers to White's, where they gave them too much to drink.

There were three occasions in Jem's life on which he behaved — it cannot be said out of character — but as if his character held qualities that were normally unseen — perhaps only vestigial qualities — yet capable, at times, of taking full charge of his great thickset body and his slow, complacent, unimaginative mind. There was that moment of decision aboard the *Impérieuse*, when the fire-ship fell athwart her; there was his strange surrender to the gentle but implacable spirit of Letitia Winslow — though that was still far ahead; and midway between these improbabilities there was the sudden genesis of his other great love-affair — his love of driving and a horse in harness.

The race on the ice lasted only a minute or two, but in that short time Jem had seen the beauty of well-chosen horses straining their huge strength to its utmost speed — he had watched Brook's firm and dextrous handling of the reins — he had felt the excitement of moving at such speed to the enchanting music of turning wheels, and now the ambition, the resolution, was anchored in his mind to drive his own cattle from his own box-seat and challenge others of a like temper to matches of speed, endurance and sheer recklessness.

His resolution was born at a propitious moment. He had grown a little tired of the undirected rowdiness of his life with Hay — he had suffered imprisonment, and run the risk of another term — and as a companion Hay was less agreeable than he had been. Hay had lived without shame on Jem's money for so long as he felt himself superior, the natural leader — but after Jem had beaten him at Jackson's he grew uncomfortable, and therefore ill-tempered — for Hay had his pride, and found it undignified to live on the charity of a man who could thrash him. About this time, the ship-chandler's widow came up from Plymouth and told a sad tale of the loneliness of her life, so Hay took the chance to show his finer

feelings, said good-bye to Jem, and went home with her. He
endured the rigours of domestic life for three or four years,
but when Cochrane went to South America, to train and
lead the Chilean navy, Hay went with him and died an
honourable death under the guns of Callao.

Now living alone, Jem wrote to Mr Brook, telling at some
length his new ambition, and with the scrap or two of worldly
wisdom he had learnt took care to add that he would soo
be in a position to bear quite easily the expense of driving,
not merely a pair of horses in a gig, but a four-in-hand. —
Mr Brook read his letter, read it again, and decided that a
young man whose opinions were so laudable, and whose fists
had been educated by Jackson, deserved all the help he could
give him; for even a bang-up Corinthian had to admit the
argument of a landed estate of £8,000 a year.

Within a very short time, however, Mr Brook's cynical
(or, at best, superficial) interest in Jem became simple,
genuine, and deep; for he quickly discovered — or so he
declared — that Jem had a pair of hands 'such as God gives
only to a true-born coachman'. They were the hands, of
course, that his sea-servitude had made for him — great
muscular hands with thick, prehensile fingers, taught to
control rough cordage and thrashing canvas — but hands
whose strength was balanced and judicious with the skill
learnt at a kicking wheel in a following sea. They were
hands that could find by instinct unseen ropes in the darkness of a howling night — and such hands had no difficulty
in knowing, at once, the off-leader's rein from the near-
wheeler's. Above them, moreover, were wrists as thick as a
fetlock and mighty forearms; he could drive all day without
wearying. 'When you have learnt to hit 'em,' said Mr Brook,
'you will have, by instruction in part and partly by gift of
nature, the ability to hit 'em and hold 'em — and that's the
making of a true coachman. But you must practise hard

with your whip. You must learn to take a fly from your off-leader's ear, bring the thong to the forefinger without looking for it, and tickle your near-leader's ribs without touching another hair. Practise your whip, and spend an hour a day with the farrier.'

Within a year Jem was driving a Stanhope gig and his own pair in tandem on the road to Salthill; and a year later he bought a drag and a team of four matched greys. This, with a spare leader and a spare wheeler, cost him £1,150, and their keep would come to some £800 a year — without a thought for his own expenses as a member, now, of the Four-in-Hand Club, and a decent obligation to waste some money on entertainment and more to the betting-book. But Jem was now master of his own fortune — though his mother and Uncle Dabney and a good lawyer still tried to keep a brake on his spending — and because his extravagances were unimaginative he found his income sufficient for his needs. Presently, indeed, it was more than sufficient, for he soon tired of fashionable life, and his growing passion for the art of driving and the life of the road absorbed him utterly.

These were the years when England became, quite suddenly, a country of brisk and vivid movement — when the long sluggishness of rural life was defeated by hard-surfaced roads, well-sprung coaches, and great stables of staunch horses in the busy inns that accommodated the new race of travellers. When travel became easy — when it was no longer a mere labour through the mud — it became also an art, a sport, a new exuberance in life; and to drive from London to Exeter or Manchester in a single day was a boisterous drama with the coachman for hero and a fanfare on the horn to summon the stage-hands at the next inn.

When the Brighton road was improved the cavalcade of high fashion gave it a tumultuous brilliance, and the

Corinthians on their high box-seats handled their ribbons and fanned their cattle with a dashing assurance that no professional driver could excel — but for a few of them the road was too easy for satisfaction. They wanted steeper hills and harder corners to demonstrate their skill and command — go to Derbyshire, they said, to prove you can hit 'em and hold 'em — and such as these not only copied the working coachmen in their dress and manner and habit of speech, but bribed their way on to the box-seats of stage-coaches and mail-coaches to show they could drive, in any weather, to the rigid demands of a time-table.

One of these dedicated drivers was Jem, who in 1823, on the Bath road, achieved a passing fame and won a bet of a thousand guineas by driving a stage-coach — as a working coachman, without privilege or leniency for his wealth — for three months unmarred by major accident or serious loss of time. This was the top and height of his career, and confirmed him, not only in his devotion to it, but in a quiet and withdrawn arrogance. He had never had much gift of speech, and now he wasted little time on words, except to farriers, ostlers, and inn-keepers. Like a coachman, he drank only gin and water — drank a good deal of it — but showed no sign of intemperance except in the growing coarseness of his appearance. Roughened and reddened by the weather, his cheeks began to extrude, as it seemed, bright rubies of hard flesh, and between his low-crowned hat and the many capes of his great driving-coat his face shone through fog or driving rain like a blacksmith's forge. He drove far and wide about England, and spent large sums of money on new teams of horses, but spent little else except on betting. He never refused a challenge or a wager.

For a dozen years or so this curiously limited but intense and fervent life gave him an apparently perfect satisfaction, and perhaps the sort of happiness that a sperm-whale in the

Antarctic, or a hippopotamus in Lake Victoria, may more dimly be aware of in its consciousness of an environment ideally furnished for all its needs. He had a woman in London, who kept house for him, and in twenty different inns he could depend on finding a chambermaid who would not expect him to make pretty speeches to win her favour. His fame on the road was such as to make all who lived on the road eager to serve him, and his knowledge, both of horses and those who attended them, prevented him from being cheated. To servants he was hard and generous, in bargaining he was shrewd but lacked the patience to take advantage of his shrewdness, and to his superiors in rank his incivility was natural and seldom resented.

From this strenuous yet placid existence he was suddenly removed, for ever, by an accident of the simplest sort. A chance encounter at an inn, where he stopped for fresh horses, a challenge to race — ten miles to the next post and a hundred guineas on it — the two coaches thundering side by side through a startled village — both swerving to avoid a child, a spill on the village green — and the following day, when Jem recovered consciousness, he was lying in a small and prettily furnished bedroom with his left arm and his right leg in splints.

There was nothing remarkable in that. — Two horses, with broken legs, had been shot, but Jem's passenger and his grooms had escaped serious injury, and the other coach had kept the road. — It was the commonest kind of accident, distinguished only by the fame of the victim and what happened to him.

The bedroom where he lay was a ground-floor room in the vicarage, and for the next ten weeks Jem was nursed by the vicar's wife and the eldest daughter of the house. Mr Winslow, the vicar, was a small and cheerful man, rosy cheeked, unpretentious, who found Christianity the most natural of creeds. His wife was a head taller than he, a good business-woman, devout by instinct and upbringing, and handsome as Juno. Their daughter Letitia — oldest of five — had inherited her mother's beauty, softened by her father's charm, and a radiant mind to which the changing temper of the age had given an evangelical fervour that neither her father nor her mother had thought essential to their untroubled faith.

The year of Jem's mishap was 1829, and already the century was changing, as if in preparation for the young Queen whose long reign was to fill it with great achievement and stamp it indelibly with a reputation for the respectability that she domesticated in her own Court. George IV was still on the throne, but near his death, and his eccentric brother would warm it for a few years only. Victoria was ten years old, and when she was crowned the very climate of England would change. There would be no place then for bucks and dandies and Corinthians, but earnestness and high endeavour would rule society in service to the probity of its monarch.

In the Wiltshire vicarage where Jem lay in splints — there was a good doctor there, and his leg knitted well, though the arm shrivelled — Letitia Winslow was a prophet of the age, and unlike most prophets had soft white hands, a proud and lovely face, the prettiest bosom — and Jem lay helpless, dependent on her, and deeply perturbed by so close an association with a young woman of a sort he had never met before. To begin with, he found conversation with her quite impossible — she, from the start, yearned to heal him both in mind and body — and would speak only to her mother. But after a few weeks he was more talkative than he had ever been before, and often Letitia was moved to tears when he told her something of the hardships of his service in the old *Impérieuse*. He found it strangely affecting to see her cry, and slowly he grew accustomed to her long prayers for his recovery: but he much preferred the intercession of her father, who addressed God with brevity and a light heart.

Until his accident, it had never occurred to Jem that religion was any concern of his. He knew that many people went to church, and that parsons made a living out of a habit that seemed to him inexplicable, but he had been content to let well alone and not trouble himself with what was manifestly beyond his comprehension. Now, however, he discovered that he too was involved in this extraordinary business, and in some peril for his previous neglect — Letitia made this perfectly clear, and wept more profusely over his spiritual ignorance than she had for his sufferings as a midshipman — and Jem, remote from all the comforting familiarities of his old life (the ribbons between his fingers, the strong smell of sweating horses, gin and water, the chatter of ostlers and chambermaids), was infected by gloom and superstitious fear; for he knew no arguments to answer hers, and he had not the strength of mind for contradiction. He had no appetite, and lost weight in bed; he grew pale, or almost pale, in the confinement of his room; he looked ten years younger when at last he was allowed to get up, and in the frailty of his injured body and unsettled mind he felt youthfully dependent on Letitia and her parents.

He learnt to use a pair of crutches, and his first journey was to church. Even the smallest of the five Winslow girls — Letitia was twenty, the youngest ten — showed such a knowledge of the service, such ease with her prayer-book, as made Jem feel isolated, and humble in his lonely ignorance. He could no longer live alone, and that evening he asked Letitia to marry him.

She was silent for a long time. She did not faint or cry, but for Jem's peace of mind did worse than that. She knelt in prayer — then stood, and said that if her father and her

mother gave their permission, she would be his wife; for
she felt it to be her duty.

Six months later she was mistress of his house, and for a
year or two Jem thought he was happy. His mother had not
taken to Letitia, so she and his sister (who never married)
went to live in Bath; and Uncle Dabney, who had put by a
fair competence during his trustee-ship, retired to his native
village in Dorset. Jem had the management of the estate in
his own hands, and if he had been capable of looking after it
would have had occupation enough; but nothing in his life
had prepared him for so large a responsibility — and farming
bored him — so in a short while Letitia and a land-steward
were doing all the business of the place, and Jem began to
feel the burden of idleness.

He could no longer drive even a light curricle and pair,
for there was no strength in his withered arm, and because he
had done little else but driving for at least a dozen years,
and had no resources in his mind, the hours were slow to pass,
and from dusk till bed-time was a yawning tedium — for
Letitia disapproved of drinking. She was very kind to him,
though strict in her discipline, and still she encouraged him
to talk about his youth. His father's inattention to him in
childhood she found deeply shocking, and to comfort him
said that his spiritual starvation was certainly a consequence
of that wicked neglect.

Until then it had not occurred to Jem that he had cause to
complain of his father — who, it is true, had taken no notice
of him at all — but as soon as the suggestion was made he
welcomed it, and quickly fell into the habit of telling their
occasional visitors, the few neighbours whom they saw, and
even passing travellers, 'I had a strange, unhappy boyhood,
Sir. My father had his own interests — he lived much in
London, where he had many literary friends — and to his
own children he paid no heed whatever. From this negligence

I suffered deeply — how deeply I did not fully perceive till
I came to years of understanding — and for the deficiencies
of my mind he is wholly to blame. He is indeed — and I
blame him bitterly. If I had had a better and more attentive
father, I might have a better mind to-day — and a good mind
is something to be proud of, if you have one, and to mourn,
if you haven't.'

Before Letitia married him, Jem had never considered
whether he possessed a mind or not — his hands were
enough for happiness — and it is a sad comment on her good
intentions, and the reform she certainly effected, that their
only result was to leave him idle, bored, and increasingly
miserable. His ways had been evil — violent, gross, and
sensual — but when he was cured of his evil ways he was left
with nothing at all to do: for his mind was incapable of
finding new employment.

His children were born at regular intervals — three girls,
then Eustace who succeeded him, and two more girls — and
from time to time he dandled them on his knee or tickled
their ribs; but children were so limited in their movement
and abilities, compared with horses, that he soon grew weary
of them. Sometimes he sat all day in a village ale-house, and
was carried home drunk; but then there were days of tears
and prayer, of pleading and repentance — days of shame and
stark discomfort and a recurrence of the superstitious fear he
had felt when Letitia first knelt in prayer for him — and after
a few more years the flat plain of boredom, that was now his
life, was uninterrupted even by drunkenness. He fell into a
profound melancholy, and it was with some difficulty that
Letitia kept him clean and tidy.

The last remnants of his mind decayed, and when all his
relations with the living world were severed he grew visibly
happier. Long memories of his youth returned to him, and
whenever the weather was fine he would walk all day by the

lake under the garden terraces, and across its tame domestic waters imagine he could see the enemy's topsails and a Spanish xebec running the blockade under the evening shadow of its native cliffs. He would hold long conversations with his fellow midshipmen, or take off his hat, and bow, and address Lord Cochrane in tones of the deepest respect. He gave no cause for anxiety except on rare occasions when he thought Cochrane was in danger, and led a foray to rescue him. Three or four times he was saved, in the nick of time, from drowning in the lake; for he was a poor swimmer.

When his son Eustace was grown-up, and about to marry the daughter of a northern ironmaster, old Jem was sorely perplexed by the excitement in the house, which he could not understand, and spent several days by the lake, with a spy-glass to his eye, looking for his former commander in the hope of being told what to do. One afternoon a gardener's boy, a silly child, heard him give a great shout of 'Coming, Sir!', and presently, going leisurely to see what was happening, saw his master struggling among the reeds at the far side.

He ran to help him out, but it was too late, and Jem, with his lungs still water-logged, died that evening. A doctor obligingly certified the cause of death as pneumonia, and the story was put about that he had lost his way — in broad daylight — and fallen into the lake by accident.

Letitia duly mourned him, but was fortified in her grief by the firm conviction that she had saved him from a career of mortal sin. 'The last years of his life were spotless,' she said. 'In his youth he may have been a little wild, but he lived to expiate all his faults.'

VI 'A Person From Porlock'

FRANCIS VANBRUGH used to boast that he had given to English literature one of its greatest poems, and one of its most famous lines of poetry; and whether it was justified or not, his assertion cannot be dismissed as mere bombast or the ebullience of a vainglorious temper. For he was a poet himself, and neither the great poem nor the single famous line for which he claimed credit was his own composition.

Francis, born in 1772, the elder son of Charles Vanbrugh, grew up in the climate of the Romantic Revival and the fair, false hope engendered by the French Revolution:

'Not favoured spots alone, but the whole earth
The beauty wore of promise — that which sets
The budding rose above the rose full blown.'

A tall, pale, stooping young man, frailly handsome; eager for life, eager to be loved, apparently very vulnerable, but guarded — not indeed against misfortune, but against the wounds that misfortune can inflict — by the very frailty that

seemed to leave him so open to them. He was prone to misfortune, for in spite of the sensitivity on which he prided
himself he was extraordinarily maladroit. He was for ever
tripping, falling, knocking down vases: or blundering into
delicate situations where no stranger was wanted. 'The only
measure he can tread is the *faux pas*, and his claim to nobility is
descent from the old French family of de Trop' — that is what
Charles Lamb said of him, if a local legend can be accepted.

But from all his misadventures he escaped unhurt, because
what would have hurt others went through him like hail-
stones through a cloud — spring hail through a sun-gilt April
cloud — and his blundering feet were always forgiven
because, so obviously, his head was in the skies — and from
that height how could he know what his feet were doing?
He had a poet's head: a noble structure on too long a neck,
with yellow hair clustered in curls, the innocent wide eyes
(a little stony) of a Greek statue, and a mouth that moved
easily to smiling, though he had no sense of humour.

He wore habitually — in youth, that is — a look of budding
happiness: a radiance just under the horizon.

> 'Bliss was it in that dawn to be alive,
> And to be young was very heaven' —

that might have been written for him, expressly. That he
had a weak heart and a tendency to fainting-fits endeared
him to older women and disarmed the criticism of his contemporaries. It was widely known that his father had committed suicide, in the antique Roman fashion, and that
excused, to some extent, the romanticism of his verses, which,
unlike his own appearance, were sombre, clouded, lighted
only by a lurid glare or the flames of destruction. They are
very bad, and in the family we do not discuss them.

It was inevitable that he should go to France, and it was
typical of him that, having decided to go in October, 1789 —

when he was greatly excited to hear that the embattled women of Paris had marched on Versailles — he was prevented by one mishap after another, and by repeated change of plan, from actually sailing until the spring of 1792.

He spent a night in Calais, to recover from a rough voyage, and from there wrote the first of many letters to a Mr Wordie, who fortunately kept them. He and Francis became acquainted at Oxford, and though they seem to have been widely different in character, and were wholly unlike each other in the habit of their lives, they maintained a friendship that lasted until Francis died. They seldom met — this may have preserved goodwill — but Francis, at irregular intervals, wrote long, enthusiastic, and often incoherent letters, to which Mr Wordie replied more briefly and more sensibly. He had taken orders, and after a curacy in Staffordshire was given a living in a remote part of Yorkshire. He married, had children, and rarely left home. The letters from Francis gave him, it is likely, his only close-up view of the world to which, at Oxford, he may have felt himself on the threshold. And Francis's letters must have done something to console him for exclusion from that world.

I am still quite dizzy from the motion of the sea [wrote Francis in Calais] but to-morrow I go to Paris. Not to stay there, however, for a brighter beacon beckons on the Loire. You cannot conceive the ecstasy I am in to think I now tread the soil made sacred, not only by glorious revolution, but by the divine impact of Mlle B's enchanting feet. What bliss to know she is so near! I shall not dally in Paris, you may be sure of that, but go with all haste to Blois.

I do not know who Mlle B was, and there is no other mention of her in the letters. She was probably the daughter

146

of French refugees who had left their country in the first
months of revolution, and then returned: shamefaced,
though still too hasty. She and Francis must have met in
England, exchanged some tender words — vows perhaps —
and when she went home again, he promised to follow. But
if he found her in Blois he was either disappointed or re-
buffed, for he does not speak of it. He tells of a more
momentous meeting.

He found comfortable lodgings with the widow of a notary,
who introduced him to several of her friends. He, so romantic, congratulated himself on living in a society from which
reason was not banished; for though some of the widow's
friends were republican in sympathy, some defended the
old régime, and neither party was so hot as to deny the other
side a hearing. In Blois, or that part of it which Francis
knew, there were evidently sensible people who waited to
see who would win before they decided on whom to bet.

He also boasted that he was the only Englishman living
in Blois; but in this he was wrong, as he discovered one fine
night when he was walking, either on the levee by the river,
or in the terraced gardens of the Bishop's palace; where,
perhaps, he had no right to be. His letter is confused, a
jumble of impressions, views, and history: he is enraptured
by the Tour du Foix, he is enamoured of Joan of Arc, he is
entranced by moonlight on the river — and there is a clue
to his whereabouts. It was a fine, clear night, he had a view
of the river, and presently (as we shall see) *he jumped*. So he
was probably walking in the terraced gardens.

He was in tearing high spirits, drunk on the air of France
and the exuberance of youth. In the gardens white statues
fled the black embrace of deadly cypresses, and lawns lay
blanched like beaches that impended over lesser beaches.
Here a little cliff that separated a terrace from the level
below threw a rug of shadow and had spilt a pool of ink.

I can jump that,' thought Francis, and with a whoop of delight ran three steps to the edge, leapt high, and in mid-air saw living shades within the pool of shadow: two entangled shades, the blur of a face, a pale expanse — of petticoat? he thought it was — and with a convulsive twist avoided one of several legs — a moving leg — but landed so awkwardly that he fell backward on to a yielding body. He heard a little cry of pain, he put out a hand and felt a soft, delicious bosom — Devonshire junket and the scent of violets, he absurdly says — but suddenly great fists had gripped him, dragged him to his feet, and before his eyes — closely staring, shouting from impassioned lips — he saw a face contorted with fury.

It was a long, lean face dominated by the harsh beak of its nose. The eyes were dark and passionate, the mouth loose and passionate, and the narrow jaw as hostile as the snout of a crocodile. Blasphemous and belabouring words came spouting from the angry mouth, and they were English words! The man on whom Francis had so nearly jumped was English — and what was immediately apparent was that he was very strong, and had little experience in the use of lewd and profane language. He had no more skill in swearing, in rank abuse, than a child who had learnt half a dozen rough words without knowing what they meant. But still, with vigorous ineptitude, he cursed and condemned the intruder on his love-making, and shook him as if he were riddling him in a sieve. Poor Francis was helpless in those strong hands — there was no breath in his body, no strength in his limbs, he could neither protest nor escape — and when at last his assailant had spent his fury, and with a great shove sent Francis reeling from him, Francis stood for a moment, sick and tremulous, then staggered — fainted — and fell full-length on the grass.

When he recovered consciousness, they were kneeling on

either side of him. The girl, who had tears in her eyes —
they caught the moonlight — was gently rubbing his right
hand; the man, now contrite and alarmed, rubbed his left —
and rubbed as roughly as a shoeing-smith rasping the hoof
of a horse. With a whisper of pain Francis withdrew his ill-
used fingers and said, 'I thought I was the only Englishman
in Blois, but you are English too. You were speaking
English.'

'Such English as does no credit to our country. I beg you
to forget all I said.'

'I have been learning English too,' said the girl in a soft
and pretty voice. 'I have learnt how to say *please* and *thank
you*. So please do not be angry with Mr William because he
was rough — and I will say "Thank you." '

Then Francis apologised for his intrusion, and explained
without embarrassment the boyish impulse of his jump. 'I
was feeling happy,' he said, and told them his name.

His late assailant was obviously unwilling to return the
courtesy, but the girl, with an innocent, leaping pride in her
voice — as if pride and joy were jumping through their
envelope of modesty — exclaimed, 'Mon mari s'appelle Mr
William, et moi — but no! it is more polite to speak English —
and I, of course, am Mrs William.'

Presently they took him back to his lodging, and though
Mr William showed no intention of continuing the acquain-
tanceship, his wife was still uneasy about the shock that
Francis had suffered, and promised they would call to enquire for him on the following day. 'She is pretty, charming,
with a temper of natural affection,' wrote Francis to Mr
Wordie, 'and I must own that I look with uncommon eager-
ness to the prospect of building a true friendship on so inauspicious a foundation. Of Mr William I have less hope.
There is some comfort in the knowledge that there is an
Englishman within call, if need be, but I do not expect he

will add much to my pleasure in being here. By his accent he is from the North country, and they are a set of damned, ingrown, cantankerous crabs who live there.'

Three weeks later, however, he wrote in a different vein. He had, by then, seen a good deal of Mr and Mrs William, and made three discoveries, the first and most sensational of which was that they were married only in the sight of God.

> Even this you may doubt [he wrote], for it is the nature of such a contract that there can be no evidence valid in law to substantiate the authority which is claimed for it. But if you had heard the sweet and thrilling purity of Annette's dear voice when she first told me of her certainty that their union was blessed with Divine approval, you would, as I did, have acquiesced in her belief. She is the most engaging creature, and so far from trying to conceal an illicit relationship, she is openly gratified by it, and talks of it so freely and so often as sometimes to put her 'mari' out of contenance.

His second discovery was truly important, and he owed it also to Annette. Mr William was a poet — and more than that, a poet in the throes of composition, a poet in labour! Francis had been allowed to read a page or two of verses, on which the ink was hardly dry, and he quoted a couplet that seemed to him exceptionally good:

> 'Where falls the purple morning far and wide
> In flakes of light upon the mountainside.'

In return for this favour he had shown Mr William one of his own poems, a description in high romantic terms of the natural splendours of the Cheddar Gorge, and of the awful reverence it had inspired in him. He had been much impressed by Mr William's criticism of the piece; while approving of its moral sentiment, he thought the language extravagant and artificial — an opinion which Francis appears to have accepted as admiration of his virtuosity.

His third discovery, at that time, seemed of no importance. It was that 'Mr William's' real name was Wordsworth. William was his Christian name, and it had been Annette's pretty fancy to use it for the marriage that nature had arranged without benefit of clergy, but with God's private dispensation. In this, his second letter from Blois, it is apparent that Francis has reversed his early judgment: it is now Wordsworth of whom he has most to say — what strength, what comfort he exudes, what warmth there is behind the stubborn reserve of his manner, and though in some ways he is too old for his years (he was just two years older than Francis), how hotly burn the fires of his enthusiasm! — but Annette, though he still praises her charm and recognises the kindness of her open heart, he now finds too demonstrative and without that gravity of mind which, he says, 'is, in fact, my dear Wordie, the only enduring base on which to build a true affection'.

Francis spent three months abroad, not all of it in Blois. He stayed for some time in Orléans and Tours, he visited many châteaux and wrote elaborate descriptions of them. His enthusiasm for the revolution was crowded from his mind by his growing passion for architecture and the romantic history he discovered in Gothic coigns and the courtyards of the Renaissance. He met Wordsworth's friend, the patriotic French soldier Beaupuy, but in another letter he gave two lines to Beaupuy and a couple of pages to the royal château of Blois. Wordsworth himself, however, is a constant figure and the growing admiration that Francis felt for him is clearly evident. It was, indeed, on Wordsworth's behalf that, at the end of July, he returned to England.

The marriage that God had so generously permitted was promising increase. Annette was in the family way, and

Wordsworth, though still working with intense enthusiasm on his poem — that he had decided to call *Descriptive Sketches* — was by now a little doubtful whether it would bring him the necessary competence on which to get married in the conventional, worldly way. He had no money other than a wretched allowance, and no hope of employment except in the Church. — In those days any young man who had been to the university could look for a vicarage if all else failed him. — Wordsworth had refused previous offers to help him to a living, but now, as Annette's trim figure increasingly drew attention to his growing responsibility, he admitted necessity, and after an unpleasant interview with Annette's mother, a widow who had re-married, he said he was prepared to take orders.

Both he and Annette were much disappointed by her mother. In the generous temper of the age, in the freedom so gloriously promised by revolution, they had expected that she would immediately recognise their right to private nuptials and a personal arrangement with God; and they had been greatly upset when she showed, not merely disapproval, but the utmost indignation at their behaviour. Annette had several sisters, and she may have thought that they too, encouraged by example, would form the habit of claiming God's approval for their amours — and Annette was plainly told that wherever she had her baby, it would not be in her stepfather's house in Blois.

It was then that Francis offered to help them. He enjoyed the friendship, he said, of that great potentate in the west of England, the Duke of Avalon; and the Duke, of course, had many livings at his disposal. He was, moreover, newly married — for the third time, indeed — to a wife much younger than himself, and therefore, in a mood of natural sentiment, he would surely be disposed to help young lovers in their difficulty: especially when he, Francis, had assured him of Wordsworth's moral earnestness and of Annette's sweet charm of manner.

Wordsworth protested his gratitude, Annette kissed him, and Francis returned to England and to Somerset. At Dunstan Abbey he met the new Duchess before he saw the Duke, and fell in love with her. She was cherry-ripe, bland as cream, corn-gold, blue-eyed, and luscious — a Bristol merchant's daughter — Gainsborough and Reynolds both painted her in girlhood, Lawrence some years after she married. Her conquest of Francis was immediate, and the confusion of mind in which she left him must certainly be blamed for the clumsy and maladroit way in which he presented his case for Wordsworth's preferment. A poet, he said; a young man but wise beyond his years. Fortified, moreover, by association with a young woman whose natural virtue was equalled only by her innate charm, and within her already bore the pledge of their mutual affection —

'How long have they been married?' asked the Duke — and Francis, like a fool, replied that many outworn conventions had now been replaced by natural law, and as Mr Wordsworth and Mlle Vallon were both, in spirit though not in action, adherents of the revolution —

'You mean to tell me, they are *démocrates*?' demanded the Duke.

'Undoubtedly,' said Francis.

'And she is in the family way, but they are not married?'

'In the sight of God,' said Francis —

'If God sees what I envisage,' said the Duke, 'and is prepared to put up with it, then He's more tolerant than anyone with my responsibilities can afford to be. Do you mean to say, Sir, that you seriously expect me to find a living for a rascally *démocrate* with a French trollop under his arm and a bastard in the bag as well? Oh, no, Sir! This is a Christian country, Mr Vanbrugh, and so long as I have my strength I'll keep it so — and keep *démocrates* out of Somerset!'

There, then, was an end to Wordsworth's hope of a living in the west of England — for the Duke's influence spread far beyond his own county — and it has to be admitted that Francis accepted defeat of his proposal without much visible anxiety for his friends in Blois. Francis was now intent on maintaining good relations with the Duke, so that from time to time he could have the happiness of talking to the Duchess. The happiness, as things turned out, of finding his affection well received, for in the late months of her first pregnancy, when the Duke thought it safe enough to allow her considerable liberty — he being fifty-four and she twenty-two he was at other times a jealous husband — the Duchess showed so warm a liking for Francis as might, in different circumstances, have been counted indiscreet. He was, after all, a young man whose physical attraction was by no means negligible, he had a rich estate in the county and, in Somerset, the reputation of a poet. But Her Grace's favour, though it gave him infinite pleasure, did him grievous harm.

Some six months later, when the Duchess had recovered her figure and her child was safely weaned — a Welsh girl of remarkable abundance had been its wet-nurse — he made, too rashly, a declaration of his love, and was very properly repulsed. Another young man might have sulked for a while, got drunk, and presently forgotten the rebuff. But Francis was a poet, with a poet's pride. He found it insufferable to live in the role of a rejected suitor, and the quickest, most decisive way to show that he was no such thing, was to choose a willing bride and lead her promptly to the altar. In doing this he found no difficulty — but, alas, no happiness.

I have said nothing, so far, of his domestic background, except his father's suicide; and that will be explained in due course. But now, without poaching on the preserve of another chapter, I must briefly describe the household in which Francis grew up.

He was nine years old when his father died, by his own hand, and the oldest of a family of three. His mother was a worthy woman, but of relatively humble origin, and in consequence of that — and of her late husband's curious mode of life — she had little or no association with the other landed proprietors and great families of Somerset. Francis, his younger brother, and their sister grew up quietly, seeing few others of their own sort; but in their time that was not unusual, and they had no sense of being ill-used. Their mother neglected neither them nor the estate. There were tutors and governesses for the children, and for many years the estate was managed by a land-steward of exceptional ability and quite remarkable honesty. It was commonly said that his loyalty was inspired wholly and solely by the person of Mrs Vanbrugh; but if the tale was true — that she became his mistress shortly after her husband's death, and so continued for many years — then the discretion with which they conducted their liaison reflected great credit on both of them, for it alienated none of the family.

It was to his mother, indeed, that Francis went for comfort after the Duchess had so rightly — but for him, so disastrously — rejected his suit; and when he told her that he had now no recourse but to marry immediately, for only a wife of his own could rub out the shame of being refused by another, she understood him at once and was quick to sympathise — quick, perhaps, to see that the Duchess would have less cause for complacency if Francis went promptly, and with manifest pleasure, to a willing bride.

She knew, as it happened, just the girl for him: a girl called Priscilla Dabney, whose mother, also a widow, had a large family and an embarrassed estate in Dorset. Hastily the two mothers conferred, and Francis met Priscilla. Francis

thought her indistinguishable from forty other girls who had
been brought up in country circumstances, but Priscilla
thought him — so handsome, a poet and so rich, and now distinguished by an air of remote and lonely melancholy — such
a prize-packet of a husband as she and ten-times-forty other
country girls had dreamed of since they left their nurseries.

The marriage, quickly arranged, was celebrated a month
later; and Francis made as bad a beginning as was possible.
He humiliated his bride, disgraced himself, and that in
public; though the public consisted only of a few close
friends, the two widows and their children, and those of the
servants who chose to watch the ceremony round the edge
of a door or through a window.

In the several weeks of waiting for it, the thought of
marriage had become repugnant to him, and on the few
occasions when they met he regarded Priscilla with increasing
fear. There was no distaste in his feeling for her — she was
a comely girl, with pleasant manners and a cheerful dis-
position — but the thought of committing himself to a lifetime of intimacy with this bright-complexioned, strapping,
and vivacious creature filled him with a growing dread. To
be shackled to someone he hardly knew, to make the inevitable discoveries and submit to her discovery of him —
that seemed a fate so brutal he could scarcely contemplate it.
But to revoke decision and jilt his Priscilla would let the
Duchess laugh and preen herself, gloating in the knowledge
of her power; and that was a thought less tolerable than
marriage. Marriage might be purgatory, but that he, a poet
and a *démocrate* like his friend Wordsworth, should suffer the
public scorn of a Duchess — why, that was hell.

It was, then, in a mood of great unhappiness that Francis
woke on his wedding-morning. He dressed in consternation,
he had no appetite for breakfast, and at first sight of his bride
he fainted. Fortunately he was in his own house, and all

there, except Mrs Dabney and her family, knew of his weakness. His mother had a flask of brandy ready for emergency, and Mrs Dabney, as she later admitted, never travelled without one. Both ladies went in turn to his assistance, and by the time Francis had recovered enough of his senses to stand and make the statutory promises his senses were decently drugged against the full realisation of what he was saying; and he gave no more trouble.

Priscilla showed remarkable strength of mind. She was deeply hurt by her reception, and retired to cry for a little while. Then, with a tearstained face but resolute composure, she came back as her mother was offering Francis a third or fourth glass of brandy, and reaching for it just in time, declared, 'I need it more than he does,' and swigged it off. 'More,' she demanded, holding out her glass.

There was a malicious story that when Francis woke the next morning, to find a girl in bed beside him, he fainted again; but this was quite untrue.

Though self-centred as a poet must be, he was naturally kind-hearted, and by no means incapable of sympathy. He realised how abominably he had behaved, and for several weeks did all he could to make Priscilla forget the shock of seeing him collapse when he turned to look at her. I do not suppose he succeeded, but she was certainly flattered by the attention he gave her — as well as some handsome presents of jewellery — and for a little while she appeared to be reasonably happy in a large and lavishly ordered house where she was allowed to do as she pleased.

Old Moses Vanbrugh — Francis's grandfather — who bought the house, had added wings to it when he was given a peerage and felt that he needed more visible support for his dignity. His addition now proved useful, for Francis's mother removed to one of them, and so gave Priscilla at least the semblance of being mistress in her own house. She

soon needed such comfort — the arid comfort that an appearance of dignity can offer — for the warmer sort of comfort she
had expected, and that Francis for a few weeks did give her,
soon diminished, flickered wan as firelight on a sunny morning, and then went out. Within a couple of months Francis
found that Priscilla bored him; and because he was a poet,
and prided himself on the sort of honesty that poets believe
to be their privilege, he could only conceal his boredom by
leaving home. Having acquired a taste for travel, he decided
to go to Italy and the Levant.

The difficulty of making plans again delayed departure.
He could not decide on a route, he chose and rejected a
travelling-companion. To fill in time he went on walking-
tours in Wales and the Lake District — he fainted on Plyn-
lymmon, but undeterred went on, and fainted on Scafell —
for he shared to the full his friend Wordsworth's love of
mountains and vile weather. He was still in England, though
not in Somerset, when his son was born; and in the pride of
having begotten an heir he discovered a new affection for the
boy's mother. While he was making fresh plans for his tour
abroad he lived at home for several months, and when at last
he embarked for Leghorn, in the early months of 1795,
Priscilla was pregnant for the second time.

Of his voyage I need say nothing, for his own narrative —
copious and full of curious detail — is still very readable in
spite of many passages of high-flying absurdity. There is
much in it that makes me envious. The simple arrogance,
the innocent egotism that let him entitle it *An Englishman
Abroad* — the assurance of his temper, unperturbed by the
humiliation of fainting-fits in St Peter's, S. Sophia, and the
mosque of Ibn Tulun in Cairo — the instant appearance of
an English man-of-war to rescue him when he got into
trouble in Alexandretta and the forgotten village of Tyre —
these and many other things excite an almost childish

jealousy in me, and I cannot see him as a ridiculous figure, however often I have to laugh at him.

An Englishman Abroad made him famous. He came home in the spring of 1797, it was published immediately, and in the summer he was immensely gratified to be told that the Duchess of Avalon looked forward to hearing from his own lips the story of his travels. He went at once to Dunstan Abbey, and found in his Duchess a stateliness that had not marked or marred her in the first year of her marriage. She received him most graciously — but as a Sovereign receives a Subject. She, in her own person, was more inaccessible than ever, and with romantic perversity Francis fell in love with her more deeply than ever. He did not hide his feelings — perhaps he could not — and she recognised his emotion as the tribute due to her. He read to her, he glossed his lordly paragraphs with gossiping detail and casual reminiscence; she admired, she laughed, she praised equally his initiative and his skill in words — and whenever he showed a little social initiative and tried to move into a warmer climate of words, she would call to one of her ladies, one of her courtiers (for Dunstan Abbey had now become a court, though a very small one) and tell Mr Vanbrugh to read again that last amusing page.

It happened one day that Francis picked up a copy of the Monthly Magazine, and was immediately taken by a poem called 'Reflections on entering into active life. A Poem which affects not to be Poetry.' It began:

> 'Low was our pretty Cot: our tallest Rose
> Peeped at the chamber-window.'

A small but perfect picture, he declared: and the author was someone called Coleridge. Now who was Coleridge?

To his surprise he discovered that Coleridge had lately been living not far away, in a village called Nether Stowey.

Perhaps he was still there. If Francis would like to see him, a groom could be sent to make enquiry.

The groom returned with the news that young Mrs Coleridge was still in the cottage, but Mr Coleridge — to get some peace from the baby, it was said — had gone off on his own, and was living near Porlock.

After five days at Dunstan Abbey Francis felt in need of a holiday — the discipline was too strait — and with so good an excuse as visiting another poet he rode off happily to Porlock: a long ride of nearly forty miles. The inn there was a poor place, but he, an experienced traveller, could easily put up with a little discomfort, and he was again in high spirits when, on the following morning, he went in search of Coleridge. The poet, he had learnt, was living in a farmhouse some three or four miles to the west.

He found it on the slope of a hill, a bleak, unfriendly-looking building in a bare, untenanted landscape, and the farmer's wife who came to the door looked as harsh and forbidding as the country. Francis told her who he was, told her he had come to Porlock expressly to see Mr Coleridge —

'But that you can't do,' she said, 'for he's not awake.'

'Then rouse him,' said Francis. 'It's no hardship to wake at eleven o'clock of a fine morning.'

'There's some that sleep sounder than others,' said the woman darkly; but was presently persuaded — perhaps money passed — to go in and shake her lodger and prepare him for a visitor.

In a few minutes she returned — a boy took charge of Francis's horse — and he followed the farmer's wife into what was obviously the best room of the house, and would have looked as if it had never been used — so coldly, sparsely, and uncomfortably was it furnished — had it not been for the presence, in a big arm-chair, of a singularly untidy young man. He wore a night-cap and an old flannel dressing-

gown, a little stained and torn. His dark hair hung in
dishevelled locks from the cap — which, while he slept, had
been pushed ludicrously to one side of his head — and his
eyes, heavy lidded under dark brows, were still dull with
sleep. He listened patiently, but without apparent interest,
while Francis again explained who he was, and where he had
come from. He seemed not to hear when Francis said that he
too was a poet, so Francis repeated his assertion, and Coleridge, after looking at him for a moment or two as if he were
perplexed or incredulous, leaned clumsily from his chair to
pick up a book that lay, open and face-down, on the floor
beside him. It was called *Purchas his Pilgrimage*.

'If that is so, Sir — I mean, if you are a poet,' he said, 'let
me commend to your interest this valuable history. I have
been reading it since yesterday — a toothache kept me awake,
though from time to time I mollified the pain with a draught
of laudanum in milk — it is a palliative drug, or anodyne,
that does no harm — and it was not till early this morning
that exhaustion overcame me. As it happened, the last
words I read, before sleep rescued me from my distress, were
these — these here — "Here the Khan Kubla commanded a
palace to be built, and a stately garden thereunto. And thus
ten miles of fertile ground were inclosed with a wall." —
And now, Sir, such is the fertile association of a striking image
and a receptive mind that I, while my external senses slept,
have composed a poem of two or three hundred lines — or,
perhaps more truly, I have watched a celebration of marriage
between a vivid experience and the expressions most apt for
recording it. The poem, or some large fragment of it, is in my
mind like a full-term child.'

'Then give it to the world, Mr Coleridge! Here on the table
is paper, here are pen and ink: express it, put it to paper
before you forget it. — I pray you, Sir! — And I shall leave
you for an hour, and then return. I beg you, Sir, *do it now!*'

Thus Francis, if we can believe him. These are his own words; and by his account he walked on the hill for exactly an hour, and when he returned Coleridge gave him two newly written pages, and he, first of all the world, read the poem beginning:

> 'In Xanadu did Kubla Khan
> A stately pleasure-dome decree:
> Where Alph, the sacred river, ran
> Through caverns measureless to man
> Down to a sunless sea.'

This, admittedly, does not quite agree with Coleridge's own account. Coleridge says he was awake, and had already written this fragment of his dream, when he was called out to see 'a person from Porlock', who detained him for more than an hour, by which time the rest of the poem had slipt or faded from his memory. But Coleridge, by his own admission, had drugged himself — with opium in some form or another — and his memory of events, or even perception of them, may well, on that morning, have been less than perfect; while it was Francis's favourite boast, in after years, that only by his insistent 'Do it now' was even the fragment preserved. I should like to believe Francis — and yet how typical of him if the contrary is true, and like a clumsy diver he blundered in and broke the perfect image in the stream! Well, we shall never know.

What I do believe, however, is that Coleridge was disingenuous in pretending that Francis detained *him*; it is far more likely that he detained Francis, and Francis indeed has left proof of this in his record of the conversation that ensued. Though conversation is not the proper word, for until the very end, it was a monologue — and (give Francis his due) a monologue to which he listened, and which, for Wordie's benefit, he described with an almost breathless admiration.

Never [he wrote] have I known such talk, such a torrent of information, ideas and images — at one point he said 'I have read almost everything', and almost I believed him when I heard, in the course of a few minutes, something about the Coptic ritual in Abyssinia, then, in passing, reference to the science of optics and the great lobsters of Spitzbergen — the crustacean theme recurred a moment later in a line of verse he twice repeated, 'Lutes, lobsters, seas of milk, and ships of amber' — it seemed to me mere nonsense — nor could I understand what he really meant by *pantisocracy*, though he explained it at some length. It was easier to sympathise when he declared 'The House of Commons is like Noah's Ark; few men and many beasts' — and I was struck by the insight in his saying, 'Gratitude is as bad as witchcraft, for it conjures up the ghosts of old forgotten kindnesses to haunt you.' Then I became confused, for it seemed to me that he gave Bentley, the Master of Trinity, credit for discovering the sources of the Nile: but this could not have been intended....

Francis has two more pages describing or illustrating Coleridge's flow of talk, and the animation that ennobled his face and gave him a sort of radiance. He concludes:

I had begun to think he would go on for ever, when he spoke of Wordsworth, and I at once broke in to claim friendship with him.

'But have you not seen him since he returned from France? He is living not far away. He has taken a house called Alfoxden, near Nether Stowey.'

Judge, my dear Wordie, the pleasure I had in hearing that! At once I was on fire to see him again and learn all his news, and when, at that moment, the farmer's wife came in to ask Coleridge if he wanted his breakfast or his dinner — for he had not eaten since he woke up — I took the opportunity to leave him, with the promise that we should meet again when he returned to Stowey. His little boy was teething, he said, but as soon as that was over he would go back....

For some reason that I cannot discover, Francis, in spite of his hurry to see Wordsworth, did not go to Alfoxden immediately — domestic business, though he consistently neglected it, may have summoned him instead — and if he had never gone it would have saved Wordsworth from repeated annoyance, and Francis from a ridiculous misconception that settled in his mind and grew like a tumour. Their first meeting was unhappy, and if Francis had owned even a mite of true sensibility, would have finished their friendship then and there.

His devoted sister Dorothy now kept house for Wordsworth, and in her benignity he had found peace of mind after his years of torment. But into that rustic peace — like a retriever jumping into a placid mill-dam where a patient fisherman sits watching his float — came Francis, exuberant and maladroit, to break its mirror into angry waves.

He arrived, unannounced, and found them sitting under a hedge — doing nothing, quite contentedly — in a small field beside the house. He greeted Wordsworth boisterously, as if they were the oldest of friends miraculously re-united, and Wordsworth with manifest reluctance presented him to Dorothy. She was no better dressed than a village girl, and she lacked physical attraction, the immediate appeal to a man's interest. Francis paid little attention to her, and addressed himself to Wordsworth.

'And how,' he asked, 'is Mrs William? How is dear Annette? I am impatient to see her again: I have brought her a little present. — And the child: is it a boy? She was sure it would be a boy. He must be — how old is he now?'

He prattled on, indifferent to the thunder gathering on the grimness of Wordsworth's face — terrible as storm on dark Helvellyn — till Dorothy, with a little moaning cry, turned and fled into the house.

'Why,' said Francis — now aware of the tempest he had raised, and stammering slightly in a sudden apprehension of disaster — 'Why, why, I hope no harm has befallen them? I hope they are well?'

'Never,' said Wordsworth in a terrible voice, 'let me hear you speak of them again! All I shall say is that what was given me was taken away, and the manner of the taking is my concern and mine alone. I will not permit any man to intervene, and probe and question me!'

Francis recovered his composure more quickly than his host. Francis, to be truthful about it, had rather pretended than felt so lively an interest in Annette, and having discovered that she was no longer living with Wordsworth, he was prepared to forget all about her. That Wordsworth's manner was peculiar had to be admitted — but he was a poet, and poets are entitled to their peculiarities. Had he been a man of the world (as Francis, without abrogating his poetic title, now felt himself to be) he would have learnt to discard a mistress more lightly: it was a pity that he had not acquired a proper experience, but that might come — and in the meantime Francis wanted to talk of other things. He had brought a copy of *An Englishman Abroad*, suitably inscribed, and he wanted to tell Wordsworth of his travels. He did — until Wordsworth, anxious about Dorothy, went in to see what she was doing.

They found her lying on her bed, as white as chalk, and with a wet compress on her forehead that dript unheeded to her pillow. Francis, taking one look at her, thought she was dead. A cry of distress rattled hoarsely in his throat — he felt his familiar, overwhelming sense of suffocation — and pitching forward on to the bed, fainted across Dorothy's feet.

It was this timely manifestation of his weakness — which they so mistakenly thought to be sensibility — that preserved their friendship. Seeing him in need of help, Dorothy dismissed her own weakness — as indeed was her habit — and removing the compress from her forehead, moistened it again and sponged his face. It was Dorothy, a few days later, who explained to him the true reason for William's separation from Annette.

He had had to come home, before the baby was born, because he had nothing to live on: if he had stayed in France he could only have starved. His intention had been to get money in England, in one way or another, and return to France as soon as possible, marry Annette, and bring her back. But then England declared war, and he could not go.

Francis pretended to accept this explanation; but he did not believe it. On reflexion, it had seemed to him that Wordsworth's anger, at his simple enquiry for Annette, had been quite excessive, and therefore proved a guilty conscience. — It did, of course; but not as Francis pictured it. Francis was thinking of manifest external guilt, of some criminal act. — In his travels in Italy and the Levant he had heard many stories of the crimes that passion bred, and he remembered a Neapolitan gentleman who had said, with some warmth, 'No woman will seriously blame the man who kills her because she has made him jealous; it is only the man who kills her because he has grown tired of her whom she will never forgive.' Now Annette — charming, gentle, true, and kind though she was — had seemed to Francis, when he knew her well enough to judge, the sort of woman whom such a man as Wordsworth was bound to tire of; and in France, where passion was more at home than in England, and where violence had lately been naturalised — but no, he would not push it to a conclusion! He could not say firmly that this was a likelier explanation than Dorothy's thin excuse, but the doubt remained. Suspicion had taken a lodging in his mind.

It did not, however, prevent him from visiting William and Dorothy, and when Coleridge returned to Stowey — the baby having got over its teething troubles — Francis often turned a poetic duet into a somewhat dissonant trio. I am, at this point, rather uncertain of my dates, for not all his letters have survived intact, but I think it was during this summer that two things happened: Charles Lamb went on holiday to Stowey, or nearby, and claimed to have discovered (as I have mentioned already) that Francis was descended from the old French family of de Trop; and Wordsworth and Coleridge made a selection of their poems which was presently published with the title of *Lyrical Ballads*.

One of these poems, by Wordsworth — one of the most celebrated — Francis read in manuscript, and professed himself greatly puzzled by it. It was called 'We are Seven', and as everyone knows it records, more or less exactly, a conversation that Wordsworth had once had with a little girl, eight years old, who counted her brothers and sisters and found seven. There was she herself, who lived with her mother, there were two at sea, two living elsewhere, and two buried in the churchyard: a total of seven.

Wordsworth protested, Wordsworth did sums on his fingers that came to five; but the little girl was quite unmoved and with childish obstinacy went on firmly saying, 'We are seven.'

Francis thought it over, and said, 'But you were right! Of course you were right. There were five of them — only five. The child was a fool.'

But then [he continues], and this I cannot understand, I grew aware of a change in their regard for me, as if the very temperature had changed, and because — I hazard this as explanation — my faculty of imagination was enlarged by the company of two such poets it seemed that they receded and grew in stature until Wordsworth looked like some gaunt pinnacle of rock isolated on a cold, unfriendly fell — and the plump geniality of Coleridge turned into the inscrutable stare of an Oriental idol sitting remotely in the shadow of a Chinese temple.

It was Wordsworth who spoke first.

'*Haud inexpertus loquitur*,' he said.

Then Coleridge began a very tedious discourse on the numbering of the Elect at the Day of Judgment, in which he spoke at length of the Institutes of Calvin, the metaphysics of the Sufi philosophers or mystics, demonic possession, the malignant influence of the Hand of Glory (with a recipe for it), and some strange practices in the Caribbean Sea of which a traveller from the West Indies had lately told him — concluding, at last, in this remarkable fashion:

'It may be,' he said, 'that Wordsworth's calculation was even more inaccurate than the girl supposed it. It is not beyond argument to suppose that in a true judgment they were *less* than five.'

This I took, as it was intended, for a joke — both Wordsworth and Coleridge laughed heartily, and went on laughing for longer than I thought it merited — but later in the day, when I was alone and in a mood to subject all I had heard to rational enquiry, I began to wonder *if it referred to some secret knowledge that they shared.*

What does this mean? It can, I think, only mean that Francis — already harbouring the suspicion that Wordsworth had murdered Annette — now thought he might have been so exasperated by the witless repetition of that obstinate little girl as to have killed her too. It is an hypothesis that cannot be rejected out of hand by anyone — a parent like myself, for example — who has known the infuriating chatter of jam-stained innocence in its numskulled nonage — but it was, I own, with the utmost reluctance that I first permitted, in my earliest study of Francis, a thought that he had entertained this monstrous belief. After further and more careful reading of his papers there was, however, no doubt about it.

There must have been, about this time, some interruption of his friendship with the two poets — it is easy enough to imagine a difference of opinion that became a breach which only time could cross — for in his letters of the next four or five years there is no reference to them whatever. Not until the spring of 1804 does he mention Wordsworth again, and then, surprisingly perhaps, he describes a visit to Grasmere: where he found Wordsworth happily married, though not to Annette; happy in Dorothy's steadfast company; and thrice happy in the fertility of his mind. Over that cottage by the lake the sky was cloudless — till Francis brought a shadow.

He found a lodging at the other end of the village, and he was at first a welcome visitor. In the last few years he had spent much of his time in London, where he knew many people of fashion as well as poets, painters, actresses, playwrights, and so forth: he had, that is, plenty of conversation with which to entertain the country folk. Wordsworth and Dorothy, on the other hand, were older and more assured than they had been at Stowey — they were accustomed to visitors now — and they could accept friendship as a lighter burden than it had been in youth. So, as the responsibilities of friendship weighed less, their talk went the more buoyantly.

Francis, moreover, began well with a contribution not only to friendship but to poetry. A day or two after his arrival he and Wordsworth were walking beside the lake on a morning when low-lying mist covered the water and seemed to lap on the side of the hill some forty feet above it.

They, walking on the high shore, were in a thin, uncertain sunlight, and before them, on a small promontory that pushed a foreland into the sea of slightly moving vapour, grew a great bank of daffodils touched by the pale sun. 'Why, look there!' exclaimed Francis. 'Look at that golden coast of daffodils!'

Wordsworth's thoughts were elsewhere, and Francis had to pull his arm and point, before he saw them. And then he said, 'We call them meadow-lilies in these parts.' But when they had returned to the cottage at Town End he remembered, though not quite accurately, what Francis had said, and told Dorothy that one of the pleasures of their walk had been their discovery, on the very edge of a cloud, as it seemed, of 'a host of golden daffodils.'

'But that,' exclaimed Dorothy, 'is the very sight that struck us — oh, when was it? I told you to take note of it, and you did. Yes, I remember, it was two years ago, on the shore of Ullswater — and you have forgotten it, William! Well, see to it that you do not forget again.'

So there was Francis's other contribution to English poetry — if we can believe his story, and I think we can — and how much better for him if he had left Grasmere that very day and never returned! But he had gone with a purpose, and deliberately he had set himself to establish an easy relation with the Wordsworths before he exposed it.

His old suspicion about the stubborn little girl of 'We are Seven' had been revived, not long before, by his meeting Charles Lamb at a literary party in London. Lamb, who had heard, either from Wordsworth or Coleridge, the story of their dispute at Stowey — it must have been angrier and more prolonged than is apparent in Francis's account of it — was in a mischievous mood, a little drunk perhaps, and asked him, 'Well, Mr Vanbrugh, have you learnt how many beans make seven?'

With a rather ponderous good humour Francis replied, 'I was taught, when a child, how many beans make five.'

'And little beans have long ears,' said Lamb, who almost certainly was drunk. 'You ought to have listened to the little girl who lived by the churchyard: she knows better than you — and so does that rascally Lake poet Wordsworth.'

This was enough to bring to memory his old delusion — to stir (as I think must be admitted) a latent hostility to Wordsworth, bred of that silly dispute and, perhaps, of jealousy — and now, at Grasmere, he made an opportunity to discuss again that simple poem; and finally was told where it was that Wordsworth had met the child, and her mother's name. Not the child's name — which Wordsworth said he had never known — but the mother's.

The Wordsworths, I gather, found the enquiry tedious, and Francis's persistent interest a bore; for he writes, triumphantly, 'But I had the better of them, and learnt that which I had come to learn.' And some time later he set out on what he calls 'my great investigation.'

It took him to the valley of the Wye, to a hamlet near Goodrich Castle, and of what he discovered there I can tell very little; and that is the good Wordie's fault. Francis describes his journey, the ruined castle, and an old man whom he questioned closely. He approaches the foot of the page — and the last few lines have been obliterated, or rather washed away, by a pinkish stain. Mr Wordie may have been so excited by what he read that he spilt his claret over it, and now there is nothing legible but the statement, which, shorn of its context, means nothing: *And there I found the stone....*

On the next page he asks:

Do you know those poems in which Wordsworth writes about a girl called Lucy? There is one that begins, quite in the confessional key, 'Strange fits of passion have I known', and goes on to the tell-tale conclusion:

> 'O mercy!' to myself I cried,
> 'If Lucy should be dead!'

In another, which must have been written *after the event*, there is the frank statement:

> 'But she is in her grave, and, oh,
> The difference to me!'

Now reverting to the former, it is well known to all who have studied the criminal mind that before the dread deed is enacted there is a prolonged period during which the criminal *contemplates his action*; whereas after it is done he may express either satisfaction or remorse. — But your curiosity grows impatient, you are anxious above all to know *who Lucy was*, and you will admit it passing strange when I tell you that no one knows! I have asked several of his friends — and no one knows! But I shall make certain....

And here again we are brought to a stop by the pinkish stain, for Mr Wordie's claret has soaked through both pages — he must have spilt the best part of a bottle — and all I can add is that Francis, in that last assertion, meant what he said.

A year went by (perhaps he was pursuing enquiries elsewhere) and he returned to Grasmere. With his extraordinary indifference to other people's feelings he assumed again the privilege of an old friend, visited the Wordsworths in their small and crowded cottage or waylaid William on his walks, and presently — with that semblance of blundering innocence which earlier, I think, was natural to him, but now more probably contrived — he began once more to talk of the unfortunate child who couldn't count, and said to Wordsworth,

'When, a year ago, I asked you her name, you said you had never heard it. But I think you were mistaken. I think you had perhaps forgotten, and now I may help you to remember it. For was not her name *Lucy*?'

Wordsworth's appearance, always impressive, had now become, though less than majestic, formidable, and when in anger awful — in the proper sense of the word, that is. His visitor's inquisitorial manner — or perhaps the reference to Lucy — made him angry on the instant, and when he rose to answer

his great jaws snapped at me like a crocodile [so Francis wrote], his eyes were the darkness that only lightning can reveal, and his nose hung over me like the Sophy's scimitar above the head of an inattentive eunuch. But I flatter myself that I kept my wits about me, and after a ridiculous diatribe in which he said he refused to be questioned, cross-questioned, examined and re-examined as if he were a prisoner in the dock, I told him politely that if he were not in the mood for conversation — 'I myself am often uncommunicative and would be solitary,' I observed — I would say no more, but come back some other day.

The ladies, I may tell you, were properly put out by his display of temper and the loudness of his voice. We were sitting in the upstairs room, his sister with us, and she with her hands pressed to her cheeks stood quite aghast, while his wife, who had been about some house- hold task, came hurrying up to see what the matter was, and while her child was howling its head off in the kitchen below, poked *her* head round the door with the most comical appearance.

But all was not over yet, for when I proposed to return on another day, Wordsworth quite lost control and shouted, 'This is my house, Sir! It is neither a hospital nor a tavern, it is not open to all who are sick or sorry, but only to those who know their manners and have the manners to wait till they are asked. And it will be a long time, Sir, before you are asked again!'

Courteously I took my leave — indeed, what else could I do? — and I own, my dear Wordie, that as I went down those steep and narrow stairs I was almost flinching with the fear that his great boot would come under me and hasten my departure. And now that you have heard all, tell me this: do you think such behaviour was the mark of an innocent man?

Give Francis his due — have I said that before? — he did not lack resolution. He went back to his lodging at the other end of the village, and prepared to wait and try his luck another day. In this, however, he was defeated: not indeed by Wordsworth, but by the weather. It rained for eleven days without ceasing, and Francis, who had now developed a rheumatic tendency, could no longer endure the moisture of the air. He retired to Somerset, to meditate a new campaign.

That Wordsworth was a murderer he had no longer any doubt. His mind had always been swayed by passion rather than reason, and in that age, when people of all sorts, gentle and simple, had time to think, they also had room to brood, and sometimes an idle thought took root and grew into a very stiff, outrageous conviction. So it was with Francis, and he was determined to go back to Grasmere when opportunity offered. 'Gradually,' he declared, 'I will wear him down till resistence is so thin that the truth shines through!'

In the following spring he prepared to go north again — but went to London instead. He spent two or three months there, and then heard that which prevented him from ever seeing Wordsworth again.

He went to an evening party, at 'my Lord Mulgrave's', I
think, though there was so much grandeur present I cannot
be sure who was host. 'My Lord Mansfield' was also there —
Francis speaks of him with a rather conscious familiarity —
and Sir George Beaumont. These three were patrons of the
arts, and the guest of the evening was the young Scotch
painter David Wilkie, newly come to London but already
something of a lion. Francis went with Samuel Rogers, the
banker who was also a poet, and did not enjoy the party. He
disliked Wilkie for his red hair and Scotch accent, and having
been painfully civil to him was rewarded for courtesy by
being button-holed by another young artist, or art student,
called Haydon; who with indecent relish described his
studies in anatomy. Dressed in all the authority of his
twenty years, he lectured poor Francis on the prime importance to the artist of a first-hand knowledge of bone and
sinew and muscle, and how to dissect them.

When Charles Lamb appeared — late, and a little drunk —
Francis was delighted. A man of letters was always better
company than those self-centred, oafish painters. And certainly the party grew noisier after Lamb's arrival, for he was
in irreverent mood — irreverent, that is, of human pretensions
and solemn claims — and everyone to whom he spoke felt a
nerve vibrate as Charles stroked it with his wit, or sighed a
little as some pomposity was deflated. Those who surrounded
him, attentive to his words, applauded the discomfiture of his
victims, called for his glass to be re-filled, and egged him on.

He was in a boisterous temper when he saw Francis — his
wit had become a clownish humour — but he had wit enough
to dress it in portentous gravity.

'A word in your ear, Mr Vanbrugh,' he said. 'A word in
confidence, and believe me when I say it is a friend who's
speaking. — If you value your life, don't go back to
Grasmere!'

'Why should I not go?' asked Francis.

'What you said to him, I haven't been told; but it put him in such a rage — I'm speaking of Wordsworth, you understand: that rascally Lake poet — well, he's been saying ever since, "If ever again he puts his nose" — that's your nose — "inside my door, I'll break his neck across my knee" — that's Wordsworth's knee, a bony eminence well known in the district. So don't go back to Grasmere, Mr Vanbrugh!'

'He may have said that, or something of the sort, but I'm sure he did not mean it. It was only a joke — his sort of joke —'

'Oh no! No, no! Lake poets do not joke, Mr Vanbrugh, and as for Wordsworth — well, tell me this. Five years ago, six or seven years ago, Wordsworth had so many critics and detractors in England that if you laid them end to end, those at the start of the line would have been old men by the time you came to the terminus. But where are they now? Ay, where are his detractors now? Ask the lake! Grasmere could tell a story if it would — and most certainly your life is forfeit if he sees you there.'

Neither Lamb nor Francis stayed long at the party after that. Poor Lamb got so drunk that he had to be taken away, and Francis was so shaken by his news of Wordsworth's murderous hostility that he had no spirit left for social enjoyment. A refuge, the safety of his own home, was what he wanted now — for in imagination he could see the darkness in Wordsworth's eye, that the lightning of his anger had uncovered, and the crocodile snapping of his jaws — so on the following day he posted down to Somerset, and every night for three weeks an armed gamekeeper patrolled the lawn beneath his window.

This extremity of fear, that shows in such contrast to the habit of his early life, was, I suppose, a symptom of his declining health; his heart was growing weaker, and though his tendency to fainting-fits had not increased, he was unable now for any major exertion. A pair of doctors from Bristol told him he must rest, and having rested in great comfort for three weeks, the gamekeeper was dismissed to his proper duties, and Francis recovered — or appeared to recover — his usual equanimity. But he never went back to Grasmere, and if Wordsworth's name were mentioned in his presence he showed a singular unease.

For a year or more he lived quietly among his neighbours, giving no more occasion for gossip than setting a lady's wig on fire. Though less maladroit than in youth, he was still clumsy on occasion, and he had taken a candle to show her a picture. She stooped to look at a pineapple in the lower left-hand corner — it was a Dutch canvas — and he, raising the candle, went on talking. Then her hair took light — it was an old hay-rick of a wig — but there was a bowl of punch on the table, and not much harm was done.

His only strong attachment to life now lay in his continuing love for the Duchess of Avalon. He had given up poetry after a play, on which he prided himself, had been hissed and booed and bombarded on its first night, and *An Englishman Abroad* — the book that had made him briefly famous — had had no successor. Only to the Duchess had he remained faithful, though without reward, and in the leisure of a country life his devotion was still as ardent as in his busy youth.

He had seen her constantly, in the passing years, for his habit of living much in London had only been formed after the Duke had decided to reopen his house there. Their friendship was an accepted thing, a recognised monument in the society that knew them; and Francis was often mocked for it, because it was notorious that the Duchess's virtue was quite impregnable. She had grown a little portly, and her stateliness was such that for the last year or two even the Duke had rarely been permitted to see her alone.

M   177

The Duke, at sixty-nine, was uncommonly well preserved, and about the time when Francis fell ill with fright, he took revenge on his wife, with deliberate ostentation, by setting up Harriet Wilson as his mistress. — Their liaison lasted six months, and he discharged her so handsomely that she kept his name out of her *Memoirs*. — The Duchess retired to Dunstan Abbey, and to preserve her pride re-assembled — or tried to — such a court as once she had kept there. But it was smaller, older, and duller than it had been, and only Francis retained that enthusiasm in her service — the gleam upon devotion that makes devotion honourable — which had characterised all her courtiers before her beauty was petrified in dignity. The others, said the servants, 'mostly come for their vittles', but Francis, unabashed, still attended as her faithful lover. And now, when Harriet had reduced her dignity to a fiction, Francis began to receive the favours he had been denied when they would have meant more to both of them. There were still small favours.

In the summer of 1808 he was staying at Dunstan Abbey, one of a party of eight or ten, none of whom was of great distinction, and on an evening of serene and temperate weather they sat together in the long drawing-room that faces to the west, and Francis was moved by the still beauty of the sky to speak of his life as if his life had come already to its close; though he was, in fact, no more than thirty-six.

He spoke of France in the years of revolution, and of the great hopes that had inspired all generous youth, and been disappointed. He spoke of his travels in the Levant, and of his poetry, and the drying-up of the springs of poetry. He told, with simple pride, the story of Coleridge in the farmhouse near Porlock, and the writing of *Kubla Khan*; for which, he added, all England was indebted to him. 'I have lived a full life,' he said, 'and though I have succeeded in none of the things that I once hoped would bring me success, I feel no bitterness against my fate — or against my father who bequeathed it.'

There was a be-whiskered General there, not old but worn-out by service, who said, 'Your father? I remember him, and what has he got to do with it? He died long ago.'

'And left me an example of defeat that I had to follow. Not in filial piety, but because *bon chien chasse de race*. I do not blame him, I merely state it as a fact — for how could I feel resentment when my life has been blessed by friendship with the most beautiful woman in England?'

He rose, and took the Duchess's hand, and kissed it. Conversation grew desultory after that, and following some discussion of what should be their entertainment for the next day — a picnic was proposed — they all took their candles and went early to bed.

When the house was still, the Duchess went to Francis's room. — Now she is not my subject and I have no obligation to explain her motive. I can say, without failure in my duty, that I do not know whether, at long last, she was touched by his devotion, and felt with a sudden dismay the hollowness of a dignity that could refuse such love — or whether, piqued by the old Duke's flagrant infidelity (he had taken another mistress, a girl of seventeen), she wanted coarsely to retaliate — whether she was lonely and miserable, or lustful and angry, I do not know. She went to his room, and that's enough.

She opened his door and stood by his bed, lighted by the candle she held. Francis, wakened from his sleep, sat up with a cry of fear. He looked at her with staring eyes, but did he recognise her? With her hair loose, and in a loose white gown, she must have looked like Juno or Minerva: one of the more formidable goddesses.

She put out her hand to him — a large, white hand — and

slowly, as if his spine were melting like the hot wax dripping from her candle, he fell back on his pillow.

She, more fretful than alarmed — for she knew his weakness — set down the candle on the table by his bed, and began to chafe his hands. But his hands, for all her rubbing, grew colder, and when she felt his arms and his chest, they were cold too.

Throughout his life he had blundered, and been maladroit; but never so maladroit as this. Never had a man chosen a worse occasion on which to die.

VII A Day on Bunker Hill

THE son of what is called 'a self-made man' — thank God I was spared that sort of parentage! — is not to be envied. He may inherit a great estate and have for his enjoyment all the opportunities of material pleasure, but either he will be so diminished in spirit by contrast with his successful father that he has no appetite for pleasure — unless, perhaps, a perverted appetite — or else so embittered by conflict with a domestic tyrant that he despises an easy acceptance of what is offered him, and can find no satisfaction except in some barren labour of his own that will let him out-do and outshine his excessive sire.

There is the choice: between rebellion and a new prospect of vulgar achievement — or obsequious surrender and the ironic reward of life in a land of plenty with no impulse to revel in it.

Charles Vanbrugh, second son of the first Baron Storleyford of Storleyford in Somerset, chose the more honourable alternative. At an early age he resolved never to accept the domination of his father, and because his father was equally determined to mould the boy into a habit of precise and absolute obedience, Charles lived for several years the life of an outcast: a moral outcast, an infant rebel, often beaten but able to preserve a show of defiance and cry in secret. He grew tough and cunning, learning much from the stable-boys to whom he fled, for the comfort of their uncritical friendship, from the tutors who thrashed him to keep in favour with his father.

It was the worst of these boys who taught him most: a child with a dirty and inventive mind, and an innocently gipsy face that Murillo might have painted, who did more mischief than any of the others, and never suffered for it because he was always civil to his elders and greeted authority with a willing smile before cocking a snook behind his back. He, who had never heard of Rimmon, had been born with the instinct to bow low in his house — at least once a day — and do as he pleased thereafter.

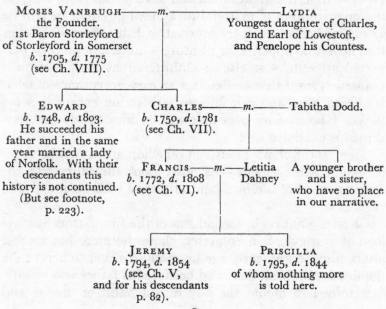

MOSES VANBRUGH——m.————————————LYDIA
the Founder.   Youngest daughter of Charles,
1st Baron Storleyford   2nd Earl of Lowestoft,
of Storleyford in Somerset   and Penelope his Countess.
b. 1705, d. 1775
(see Ch. VIII).

EDWARD   CHARLES————m.——Tabitha Dodd.
b. 1748, d. 1803.   b. 1750, d. 1781
He succeeded his   (see Ch. VII).
father and in the same
year married a lady
of Norfolk. With their   FRANCIS——m.——Letitia   A younger brother
descendants this   b. 1772, d. 1808   Dabney   and a sister,
history is not continued. (see Ch. VI).   who have no place
(But see footnote,   in our narrative.
p. 223).

JEREMY   PRISCILLA
b. 1794, d. 1854   b. 1795, d. 1844
(see Ch. V,   of whom nothing more
and for his descendants   is told here.
p. 82).

Charles, who had long admired him, adopted the same course, and at ten or eleven began to show attention to his lessons. This, as he correctly judged, was the easiest way to persuade his elders that he had now decided to conform. What he had not foreseen was that he would find his lessons interesting, and discover in himself an aptitude for scholarship. He quickly earned his father's favour, and found it easy to lead a life of secret pleasure, in whose naughty exploits the Murillo-like stable-boy collaborated, without rousing any suspicion that he was misbehaving.

At Eton he was regarded as a prodigy of learning, and when he went to Oxford he was gravely disappointed by its intellectual poverty. The college dons were incurably idle, and by prolonged indolence some had grown quite illiterate. They drank deeply, and the more they drank the duller seemed their wits. The university professors delivered few lectures, and no one went to hear them. After some years in residence, a gentleman commoner was given his degree as casually as if it were an overcoat handed him by a footman when the party was over.

To Charles the prospect of such torpor was unbearable. He had found his ambition, and made no secret of it. To become a scholar was only the first step: he must learn the philosophies and history of Greece and Rome, their policies as well as their languages, to equip himself as a senator in Britain. He saw no hindrance to his advancement. From infancy he had heard familiar talk of the greatest in the land, and none of them, it seemed — none but William Pitt — was of such a stature as demanded more than a passing respect. Already he could measure himself against most of them, and in a few years' time, when he had shaped and prepared himself for office, he would not balk at the highest. Prime ministers did not last for ever, and when the country looked to him he would be ready for his task. Scholarship first, and then a few years in one of the armed services: coldly and with assurance he had devised his education, for he knew that book-learning alone did not breed authority. The knowledge and habit of command were also desirable.

There was a poor student called Rowlandson with whom, by accident, Charles became acquainted, and in whom he found a hunger for learning that matched his own, though Rowlandson had no worldly ambition to encourage it, and a knowledge of the classical authors that already shamed the fellows of his college. Charles, who had a lavish allowance from his father, engaged Rowlandson as his tutor, and with his help and advice began to collect a classical library that soon numbered four or five hundred volumes. He and Rowlandson formed a private school, within the university, and regarded their nominal teachers with a distant contempt.

They did not, however, give all their time to books. His expressed intention of acquiring some experience of war, as the next stage in his education, made it clearly evident to Charles, but less so to Rowlandson, that they must spend two days a week on horseback. There were, near Bicester, a long-established pack of harriers, and a lately formed pack of fox-hounds. Which gave the better sport was a matter for dispute, but fox-hunting demanded more riding, and Charles insisted on their following the newer sort of hounds. He was generous to Rowlandson, and not only mounted him well but saw that he was decently dressed in a blue coat and properly cut breeches.

Rowlandson was a poor horseman, and though loyalty to Charles kept them in company for a season, he broke away in their second year, and chose to follow the harriers: not on horseback, but on foot. This decision provoked a consequence of the greatest importance.

Living near Bicester was a well-to-do yeoman farmer called Dodd, whose name was hallowed in the district. Not, however, for his well-tilled fields, but for his three lovely daughters, the fairest of whom was Tabitha the youngest. From the orchard below the farmhouse she was watching the hunt one day, when she saw a young man running hard across a field on a line well-judged to meet a hare that was turning in a left-handed circle, with the hounds not far behind; and suddenly she too was running. The young man had tripped and fallen, and Tabitha, who was tender hearted, hurried to help him. Rowlandson, with a twisted ankle, spent the night at Farmer Dodd's, and soon formed the habit of losing the harriers to go and look for Tabitha.

He was discreet, and for almost a year said nothing of his passion. But one day, finding him disconsolate and woebegone, Charles pressed him for a reason, and Rowlandson admitted that he was over head and ears in love with a girl, and because of his poverty saw no chance of being able to marry her. Despite the habit of coldness that he cultivated, Charles was not so cold that he could restrain his curiosity, and he soon persuaded Rowlandson to take him to meet Tabitha. They rode together, on their first visit, and the farmer's handsome daughters gave them a hearty welcome and quickly had them dancing in the barn to a lively fiddle-tune.

Within a few weeks Charles was riding alone to Farmer Dodd's, and of the three sisters it was Tabitha that he too went to see. She, poor girl, presently found herself in a quandary, for though she had thought herself in love with Rowlandson, she now suspected herself to be more truly in love with Charles. Charles, who always knew what he wanted, knew with the certitude of passion that only Tabitha could make him happy; and because she was virtuous he offered to marry her. Indeed, he demanded marriage, and that as quickly as could be contrived. The prospect of marriage undoubtedly woke in Tabitha's heart a livelier warmth than Rowlandson had stirred, but she had in some sort pledged her word to him, and in a flood of tears declared she could not break it. Only if Rowlandson abandoned her would she account herself free.

Now Charles revealed his strength of mind and sense of mastery. To Rowlandson he spoke at great length, and with consummate skill, of the charms of Deborah, the eldest sister. He dwelt, most movingly, on the hurt she would suffer to see her youngest sister married before her, and such was his admiration of Deborah, so deep his regard for her, that he would, he said, most gladly give Rowlandson £500 and the promise of a parsonage on his brother's estate in Norfolk if he would concur in a simple act of justice, to a family they both held in high esteem, by offering marriage to the eldest daughter.

Rowlandson was no fool. He took another look at the three sisters and thought, a little sadly, that in ten years' time there might be not much to choose between them. But for the present there was a mighty difference, for if he could love Deborah he would be vastly enriched and settled for life; whereas to continue in love with Tabitha meant only heartbreak, frustration, and lasting poverty. He made the sensible choice and set Tabitha free to marry Charles.

She made no objection when Charles told her that their marriage must be kept secret, and her parents were persuaded of the wisdom of discretion when Charles, again with much eloquence, described his father's dictatorial temper and the ruin of his prospects that a marriage based on love alone would certainly provoke. Farmer Dodd insisted on being present at the ceremony, to be sure that Tabitha was made an honest woman, and as it was easy, in Bicester, to find a parson who thought the publication of banns a mere irrelevance, Charles and Tabitha were made man and wife without any advertisement and in the privacy of the farmhouse.

Charles removed his library to a small house in Burford, where in contentment and peace of mind he continued his studies for a couple of years. He did not condescend to take a degree. Without forfeiting his father's trust he maintained the secrecy of his marriage, and fathered two sons. To be nearer London, he presently went to live in Tunbridge Wells, and increasingly congratulated himself on the wisdom with which he had chosen a wife. Lively and affectionate in private, Tabitha conducted herself with a grave deportment in public, and accepted without demur his insistence on the continuing necessity of discretion. Perhaps it added to her happiness, to think that her marriage was still clandestine, and therefore romantic; while Charles had the comfortable feeling that every time he went to bed he was flouting his father's authority and living by his own arbitrament.

He and Tabitha had no quarrel until, in 1773, he persuaded his father to buy him a cornetcy in the Life Guards. This was the first step in the second phase of his chosen course of education, and Tabitha could see no point or purpose in it. Hotly she denounced the folly of all soldiers, the bitter waste of war, and coldly he explained the advantage of acquiring some knowledge of an activity that human nature and the demands of history had shown to be essential. For some months they were hardly reconciled, and dispute was renewed, more fiercely and with profounder grief, when Charles's commission in the Life Guards was exchanged for a captaincy in the 5th of Foot.

War with the American colonists was now imminent, and Charles was determined that so fine an opportunity for gaining experience must not be missed. Tabitha, who was pregnant again, thought otherwise, and when, in January

1775, Charles left her to go aboard a transport that was under orders for Boston, they parted in sorrow and anger.

There were those who believed the American colonists to be men of high principle, irrevocably addicted to the pursuit of liberty and the practice of virtue, who would rather die in defence of their principles than live in submission to a remote authority which, however tolerant in practice, was unjustified in nature. Foremost among those who expressed a high opinion of the colonists was the Irishman Edmund Burke, whom they paid for his laudations. But others said the Americans were a set of congenital malcontents, lawless by nature and tax-dodgers by habit, who had no motives more commendable than a loutish distaste for authority and a street-trader's nose for the illicit profits that a government of their own would make possible by the venality of its character and the impotence of its constitution. Of those who delivered so uncharitable a judgment some may have been disappointed by the colonists' failure to subsidise them, as they had subsidised Burke, but many were inspired by a simple, indignant anger with people of their own blood who refused to acknowledge common obligations and a common loyalty.

Typical of these was Charles Vanbrugh. To him, who aspired in the ripeness of time to become prime minister of Britain and extend its greatness in proportion to his own, it was intolerable that his empire should be curtailed by the senseless rebellion of a mannerless rabble who subsisted, in a tempered squalor, on smuggling, piracy, and the products of their primitive agriculture. The reinforcements for which General Gage had asked did not reach Boston till May, for the government, being unprepared for war, had had the greatest difficulty in finding men; and by that time Charles was impatient almost to the pitch of frenzy. To some extent he had lost sight of his original intention, which was to learn a little of the art of war, and he was now more eager to teach the insurgents a lesson: to teach them, as quickly and severely as possible, the lesson of obedience to Britain and its future prime minister.

In Boston he went ashore with General Howe, and it soon became evident that General Howe shared not only Charles's opinion but also his temper. For when it was seen that the insurgents had put themselves in a position where, with perfect ease, they could be exterminated, General Howe and his staff declined an exercise so obvious, and prepared, by demonstration, to instruct the rude Americans in the fine tactics of the drill-ground.

Like a ragged leaf on its stem, the narrow-necked peninsula of Boston grew into the bay, from whose north-western corner came, as if to meet it, the triangular leaf of Charlestown on a stalk as slender. On the Charlestown leaf there was a small hill, called Bunker Hill, from which Boston might be bombarded; so General Gage resolved to occupy it. But the Americans in Boston heard every word that was uttered in the General's headquarters, and before Gage had moved, a strong American force advanced by night into the Charlestown peninsula and skilfully entrenched on another hill. This was Breed's Hill, and had the advantage of being nearer to Boston than Bunker Hill.

The Americans, after working all night to dig trenches and throw up a redoubt, had installed themselves by morning, with patent success, in a perfect trap. General Gage had command of the bay, and to destroy the insurgents all he had to do was to cut the stem of the Charlestown leaf, which was only two hundred yards across, and let a couple of gunboats enfilade the entrenchments. But after conferring with General Howe he rejected this easy plan and decided to make a frontal attack; which would have the double advantage of being difficult, and of giving his soldiers a chance to show their discipline.

The troops were disembarked at the outermost tip of the leaf, and formed up in three lines. The soldiers carried full packs and three days' rations: there was no apparent need for such burdens, but General Howe, who commanded the landing force, was determined to leave nothing to chance: not even casualties. The soldiers in their scarlet tunics made a handsome show as they advanced through the long, thick grass, over ground broken by fences, and a scorching sun enhanced the brilliance of their uniforms. The Americans had no such advantage. The Americans, under cover, could not be seen at all; but their riflemen, taught from infancy, in their wild way of life, to handle weapons, poured a deadly fire into the redcoats, and their marksmen took as their favourite targets the officers whose golden epaulettes so clearly distinguished them.

The advance was halted, and the British troops retired a little way to re-form their ranks. On their left wing, where Charles led a company of his regiment, snipers had been shooting from the close-packed houses of Charlestown, and now a battery on the north shore of Boston opened fire on the houses, which burned well and sent out hot clouds of smoke to increase the redcoats' discomfort. Their own field-guns could give them no support, for they had been supplied with cannon-balls of the wrong size.

But again the infantry advanced, in the same formation, though thinner on the ground, and with a discipline hardly impaired. Again they suffered heavy casualties, without seeing much of their enemy, and within a few yards of the American defences the attack hesitated, crumbled, and broke. Only on the extreme left did a little desperate party of the 5th reach and break into the trenches. It was Charles who led them; and they were not seen again.

190

General Howe had lost all his staff, but he himself was un-
wounded and unimpressed by losses. He ordered his men to
take off their packs, and advance for the third time. But this
time, he said, let there be no shooting. Let them trust to their
bayonets.

Their scarlet tunics now dark with sweat — black squares
of sweat where their packs had lain — the indomitable
infantry returned over the trampled grass, in silence now
behind the high-pointed menace of their bayonets. Their
exhaustion was pressed down and out of sight by fortitude,
and bitterness of spirit, and the lessons of the drill-sergeant.
They stepped over their dead and steadily drew nearer to the
trenches. The Americans fired their last volley, and thinned
again the scarlet ranks. But throughout the battle the
Americans had received no reinforcement, neither of men
nor ammunition — their own comrades had stood idly on the
landward slopes to watch their battle — and now, when they
had fired their last rounds, there were few who stayed to
fight it out. Here and there a little group still faced the red
bayonets, but the majority fled fast round the slopes of
Bunker Hill, and under the fire of the British warships over
the neck of the peninsula — the stem of the leaf — to safety
and the wild applause of their fellows.

Of the twenty-five hundred British soldiers who had gone
into battle, more than a thousand were dead or wounded,
but General Howe's demonstraton of their steadiness under
fire and their impeccable drill had been entirely successful.

Among those reported dead — though his body had not
been found — was Captain Charles Vanbrugh of the 5th of
Foot.

The brothers Paul and Silas Liversedge were admirable as
pioneers. They were good shots and skilful trappers, they
could find their way through virgin forest and in a birch-bark

canoe navigate the dangerous rapids of a fast-running river. Lean and sturdy of body, their minds also were lean rather than broad, and sturdy rather than sensitive: they had adopted many of the habits of their Indian neighbours, and among possessions so few that an ascetic would have applauded their austerity, each owned a couple of human scalps.

Their sense of humour, though positive, was extremely limited. When Charles Vanbrugh came charging over the earthwork and leapt into their section of the trench on Breed's Hill, Silas quickly swung the butt of a long musket round to meet the bone under his left ear with a resounding blow, and as he lay unconscious the brothers looked down at him with gloating eyes and identical thoughts. They had taken a prisoner — an English officer — and what could be more triumphantly humorous than to parade their captive through Cambridge, Lexington, and Concord? They resolved to waste no more time on the battle, and as discipline on the American side was lax, they had little difficulty in making a private retreat before the British infantry attacked for the third time. Charles, only lightly stunned, recovered sufficient strength to walk, stumbling and dull of sight, with the assistance of Silas on one side and Paul on the other.

That was the beginning, for him, of a period of extreme hardship and intense humiliation. The brothers, after enjoying to the full their tour of Cambridge, Lexington, and Concord, discovered a new and even richer joke. They would employ Charles as their man-servant. He had no chance of escaping this abominable servitude, for not only was he in a hostile country, but each of the brothers was far stronger than he, and he had no weapons. They took him to a cabin in some desolate valley beside a river that may have been the Connecticut; but Charles, not unnaturally, spoke very little about his years of captivity, and it can only be conjectured where he spent them. What is known is that he endured a winter of extraordinary discomfort with the brothers, and in the following summer, when they decided to re-join the army, they sold him to an elderly couple who lived a little farther to the west: perhaps near Lake Champlain.

The husband was a kindly soul, but the woman treated Charles with great brutality; and eventually her cruelty secured his release. It came to the ears of a neighbour who knew enough about the British to have no sympathy with their cause, and so much about his fellow-colonists that he disliked the prospect of their victory. He was filled with indignation to hear that a helpless captive was being ill-treated, and as he and his family had decided to start a new life in Canada, he resolved to take Charles Vanbrugh with him. He had three well-grown sons, and the rescue presented no difficulty.

It was the autumn of 1777 when Charles at last came home, and found himself bereft of a father but heir to a large estate in Somerset. His father, who had been in poor health since the loss of his wife, had died shortly after hearing of Charles's supposed death on Bunker Hill, and Edward, his elder son, had succeeded to the title and a wide domain in Norfolk. But the estate in Somerset had been Lord Storleyford's favourite property, and that had been left to Charles, his favoured son.

Tabitha and the children were living with her parents at Bicester — old Storleyford had died without ever hearing of their existence — and she, in a rapture of delight to hear that her husband was still alive, decided there and then that his deliverance was directly due to a heavenly intervention. It was fortunate indeed that she adopted this belief, for the remaining years of her life with Charles were extremely difficult, and without such a warrant for his escape it is doubtful if she could have endured the isolation on which he insisted. The children openly resented his return, and though in a sullen way they became reconciled to his presence, they gave him no affection and he did nothing to endear himself to them.

As soon as possible, Charles established himself and his family in the great house in Somerset, which his father had notably enlarged, and in a mood of the gravest sorrow — which, however, was enlivened by a persistent anger that he made no attempt to curb — he settled down to a task for which his early life had well equipped him, and which, as he now perceived, was his destined service to England.

Perhaps it is impossible to realise how deeply he had suffered in his American captivity. The physical hardships were extreme, but he was young, and the memory of them he could have sloughed in time. What was ineradicable was the spiritual humiliation. That he, an Englishman of high rank — almost of noble rank — should have been reduced to serfdom, and sold like a serf, by those untaught, brutish, and detestable colonists: that was truly intolerable! And wider and deeper than his own humiliation — surrounding it like a storm-bound, sombre coast and receding behind it into a very abyss of shame — was the humiliation of England itself. Those abominable colonists were going to win their war.

In one way only could Charles hope to save his country from the collapse and doom that were, unless it took timely warning, its ineluctable end. He had failed in war, he had blunted his sword to no purpose, but his pen remained, and that in his youth he had sharpened by scholarship to a cutting edge. He would write the history of Rome's collapse — Rome, the centre of that other imperium which, by self-indulgence and the neglect of virtue, had so weakened itself as to let in the destroying tides of barbarism — and if, as he could, he wrote that story with anger to impel him and sorrow to give it depth, he might awaken England to its peril and save his country on the very lip of doom.

For such a task he had, in his own house, the necessary apparatus. There was the considerable library, carefully preserved by Tabitha, that he had collected at Oxford, and there was a more numerous library that his father had bought, as necessary furniture, when he enlarged the house. But he must have privacy for his work: an absolute, un-assailed solitude — and to Tabitha was given the duty, hardly less onerous than his own, of creating and assuring the perfect isolation in which, for his country's sake, he could create his masterpiece.

Tabitha did not hesitate. She prepared to immolate her-self, and did. The whole household, the whole estate, were so organised as to give Charles the freedom of a hermit and the security of a feudal count surrounded by his battlements and loyal retainers. And Charles, with a fervour that the years did not diminish — with sorrow unallayed and anger that every morning woke renewed — addressed himself to his work. On the tables in his library, and spilling from tables to the floor, lay folios and quartos, the sepulchres of cata-strophe from which he disinterred old bones to put upon them the flesh of modern instances: Livy and Macrobius, Tacitus and Seneca and Dionysius of Halicarnassus, Juvenal, Polybius, Cicero and Suetonius, and how many more? To all these jawbones, dead and buried, he gave his clamant, living voice.

The years went by, and Charles, untouched by the world about him, knowing little or nothing of its absurdities, its pettiness and frail achievement, finished at last the first volume of his history. He called it *The Collapse and Doom of Rome*.

It was in 1781 that he entrusted his manuscript to a faith-ful servant, and sent him with it to a bookseller in the Strand. Charles himself could not afford the time to undertake such a journey, for he was already at work on volume two. But he had written a letter to the bookseller in which he recommended his manuscript, not only for its intrinsic value, but its substantial importance in a contemporary way; and with confidence, he said, he would await the bookseller's offer to publish it on terms agreeable to them both.

Patiently at work on volume two, untroubled by doubt, he waited for a reply; and when, after a considerable delay, it arrived, he had to read it three or four times before he could believe it.

Though he had perused Mr Vanbrugh's work with much admiration, said the bookseller, he thought it unlikely that the public would subscribe to *another* history of the decay of Rome and its Empire. It was some years since he had published the first volume of Mr Gibbon's narrative, and to that, within the last few weeks, he had had the happiness of adding volumes two and three. As Mr Vanbrugh was interested in the period, he was sending him the three volumes in a separate parcel, and trusted that Mr Vanbrugh would become a subscriber.

Poor Charles unwrapped the parcel and discovered three large, square, leather-bound volumes of a work entitled *The History of the Decline and Fall of the Roman Empire*, by Edward Gibbon, Esq. He opened the first of them and read: 'In the second century of the Christian Era the Empire of Rome comprehended the fairest part of the earth, and the most civilized portion of mankind. The frontiers of that extensive monarchy were guarded by ancient renown and disciplined valour...' He turned the pages to read of the fury of the barbarians, 'who seemed to fall from a new world', and by the energy of their primitive fervour breached the walls of that monarchy of old renown...

It was all there. All that he had laboured to excavate and display was there. His labour of the last — how many years? two, three, four — had all been wasted. The years he had given to scholarship had brought forth dead fruit only, and a monument to redundancy. His whole life recorded failure.

He spent a day or two in contemplation, and from the ruin of his days retrieved two thoughts for comfort. He had, by exercise, achieved a Roman spirit of the ancient Roman sort — the spirit of Regulus — and in defiance of his father's authority he had married a good wife.

He went to see Tabitha, and told her that his labour had come to nothing. She gave him sympathy, but could not understand the measure of his disaster. She listened patiently, however, while he explained that the beginning of his misfortunes had been a boyhood spent in the shadow of his father's greatness. It was that shadow which had chilled his blood, and all his endeavour had been to build for himself an eminence from which he could look down upon it, and know that he was above its coldness. But his endeavour had been defeated.

He thanked her for the devotion she had given him, and said good-bye to her. This also she did not understand.

In the grounds of his fine house there was a lake, and meandering to feed it came a little stream that chattered on bright pebbles and sparkled in the sun. With a mien of perfect composure Charles walked towards it, to a shallow pool that spread beneath a weedy shelf of rock, and took off his coat and shirt. The day was warm, and he did not even shiver as he sat down in the pool, leaning comfortably against the shelf of rock, and took from a pocket in his breeches a small, sharp knife.

He uttered no valediction to his life and the world in which he had lived it, for he did not account them worth the compliment; but with a calm deliberation and a steady hand cut the artery in his left wrist, and then, taking the knife into his left hand, a little clumsily but deeply cut his right wrist.

He let his hands fall into the running stream, and for a moment or two watched the thin fountains of bright red blood leap into the greenish water, and dissolve in its flood. And there, thank God — such was his last thought — is the end of that.

VIII The Founder

Our original patron — it would be nearer the case to say *originating*, for in a way he was our progenitor too — was the second Earl of Lowestoft,* whose grandmother was the actress Kitty Fitzsimmons; and, to begin with, something must be said of her.

While still very young she achieved a small but agreeable fame when the theatres were re-opened after the restoration of Charles II, and by some private display of her amiability she won also the brief favour of the King. She returned to the stage two or three years later, and after a succession of dull, unrewarding parts, made a considerable reputation by the apparent innocence with which she portrayed the licentious heroines of England's first woman dramatist: that pioneer of feminism, Aphra Behn.

* The title is extant, but the estate has vanished. The Earl of Lowestoft to whose niggardly hospitality I refer on page 237 was 14th in succession. His son, the present Earl, is farming in Southern Rhodesia.

In 1681 or 1682 Kitty Fitzsimmons married a gentleman of Suffolk, a good deal older than herself, whose enormous wealth was derived almost equally from North Sea herring and the wool of his innumerable flocks of sheep. Being persuaded that it was necessary to live in London, he took a house on the river, not far from the Savoy, and such was the splendour of his establishment that he soon attracted the attention of the King; whose pleasure in finding Kitty so comfortably established was manifest and unaffected.

The child whom she had borne to Charles was now a spirited and handsome young man who flattered his royal father by an unmistakable resemblance to him and a gay intelligence that made his Stuart blood obvious to everyone who was clever enough to say so. Kitty, with a gifted son, was naturally ambitious for him. Her old husband was utterly devoted to her, and his riches were immense. The King, as always, was in need of money. There, clearly, were the foursquare foundations of an Earldom; and the title of Lowestoft was chosen by Kitty's husband — not for himself, but for his stepson — to whom he promised an endowment equal to the sum of money which the King had so graciously accepted from him.

Edward, first Earl of Lowestoft, married prudently but died young. Charles, the second Earl, entered his inheritance at the age of nineteen and married for love the beautiful but penniless daughter of an Irish lieutenant, in the naval service, who had lost a leg in action against the pirates of Algiers. Her name was Penelope — there were scholars in the family as well as crippled lieutenants — and she and her husband became the sponsors, patrons, parents-in-God and prime benefactors of all us Vanbrughs. It happened in this way.

On October 30th, 1705, a new play called *The Confederacy* was presented at the new Queen's Theatre in the Haymarket, and a fortnight later the play was in print and on sale. It was, then, on a day subsequent to November 15th, 1705, that the first of my family — my earliest known ancestor — made his amply recorded entrance into history: his 'birthday' (if such it can be called) was sometime between then and Christmas.

How often *The Confederacy* was performed I do not know, but it was popular, and both Mrs Barry and Mrs Bracegirdle acted in it. To one performance went the young Earl of Lowestoft and his wife — so much in love that they dared flout convention and be seen in public together — and a friend who accompanied them (a hanger-on, a fellow half useful to them, half a mere sycophant: Colley, by name: something of a scribbler) wrote, in a letter that has survived,

My Lady was overcome with laughter, so often and so far beyond restraint, that presently she began to shake and cry with mirth, and My Lord, for fear she would do worse and make a spectacle of herself, resolved that only by giving her a great shock could he restore her to her senses. This he did by turning suddenly and kissing her so fondly that those near enough to see what he was about applauded him loudly. Poor Mrs Bracegirdle was sorely put out and forgot her lines, while My Lady was compelled to forego her own emotion to govern his, he having whispered to her that his passion had been excited beyond measure or mastery by envy of an author whose mere words could move her so extremely. My Lady grew contrite, My Lord consented to be pacified, and with hands enclasped they sat quietly till the play reached an end.

Thus joined in love, armoured against the world in love, they waited while Colley went to find their coach. They waited patiently — the traffic was thick — and then went in search of Colley and found him arguing with the coachman whose breath stank of gin, with a groom who was drunk, and with a little ragged boy who had been holding the horses. The coachman said they had been cajoled and led astray by a gentleman who claimed to be a great friend of His Lordship — the groom wept and swore never to touch strong waters again — and His Lordship, still in good humour, said they had better walk home (it would be good for their health) and leave him to drive. Colley opened a door for Her Ladyship, our dear Penelope, and nimbly His Lordship set foot on the hub of the near front wheel to leap on to the box. But before he could make another move Penelope gave a cry of shrill, excited surprise, and a moment later he too was gazing, bewildered, into the basket that she had discovered on the front seat of the coach.

The child in the basket was about six months old, clean and well nourished, wrapped warmly in a shirt that had been much darned and a blanket somewhat threadbare and yellow with age. He gurgled happily at the attention he received, and smiled enticingly when Penelope bent above him. 'We must take him with us,' she exclaimed. 'Hurry, oh, hurry! Perhaps he is hungry.'

Colley said something about the Foundlings' Hospital, but Penelope looked at him contemptuously and again begged her husband to make haste. 'But drive carefully,' she added, 'for he must not be frightened.' Her husband shrugged, and said to Colley, 'He isn't mine, I wonder if he's yours?' He did not wait for an answer — Colley was sourly offended — but climbing to the box took the reins, threw a coin to the little ragged boy, and drove smartly out to his new house in Grosvenor Square — where, indeed, none of the houses was much more than ten years old.

There the baby in the basket was numerously attended, combed and cosseted, fed and re-clad — a warm and bustling housekeeper who had buried two of her own took principal charge — and His Lordship was much amused, Her Ladyship awe-struck by the coincidence, when at the bottom of the basket there was found a rather grubby copy of the play they had just seen: *The Confederacy*, by John Vanbrugh, not yet a knight.

There is no doubt at all that Penelope had decided, almost at first sight, to keep and look after the child thus thrust upon them; and her husband, good-humoured and deeply in love, cannot have seriously opposed her. If Colley is to be trusted, they went farther than that. Colley was not, I think, a likeable creature — though his patrons appear to have liked him well enough — but in fairness it must be said that he showed for many years a constant care for an invalid sister who lived alone, but for one elderly maid, in Long Melford. To her he wrote regularly, and it is to his letters that I owe most of the substance of this story: or rather, of its early part. And according to Colley it was Penelope's intention to adopt the child and bring him up as her own.

They called him, at first, 'the little Vanbrugh', after the author of the comedy they had seen, of the play-book that was so strangely found in the child's basket. (They assumed, says Colley, that one or other of his parents was a player; and perhaps both were. So poorly clad, but clean and well-fed: had they abandoned their baby in utter grief, too poor to keep him?) — And then, having found a surname, they must think of a Christian name; His Lordship, in facetious mood, said, 'The basket is all we have for guidance, let us call him Moses.' Penelope protested, but not much, and His Lordship got his way. And the joke was given permanence when Penelope had the child baptised.

It is amusing to conjecture what might have happened if Penelope had remained childless, and persisted in her first intention to adopt him. That, however, began to fade and

grow less in the early months of 1707, when, after three years
of marriage, she found herself pregnant. For some little time
after her own child was born she forgot all about Moses, who
would have been sadly neglected had it not been for the
warm housekeeper. Presently he was taken into favour
again, and regarded as a possible playmate for the little
Viscount who lay so snugly in his satin-lined crib; but that
prospect vanished also when, year after year, Penelope
ripened in the spring and was regularly brought to bed
between Guy Fawkes Day and Christmas. It was Mrs
Crambo, the housekeeper who had buried her own, who
assured a due provision for him by finding him employment
in His Lordship's establishment; which was so large that an
extra boy or two made no noticeable difference.

In the household of a great nobleman of those days there
was a recognised hierarchy: intricate, ordained, but permeable to talent. And Charles, Earl of Lowestoft, was great
indeed — in the second or third order of greatness — for he
had inherited not only the original endowment of his father's
title, but, through his grandmother (the innocent actress of
Aphra Behn's lascivious heroines) the whole, vast estate of
the old Suffolk gentleman she married; who, most fortunately, had died without issue. Charles, therefore, succeeded to a minor regality within the kingdom of Britain,
and had his own ministers, officials, servants and drudges.
His upper servants, indeed, had servants for themselves, and
at the age of eight Moses, in livery, became footboy to Mrs
Crambo the housekeeper.

At dinner and supper, in imitation of their betters, he
stood behind her chair, and among the first of his lessons
learnt the order and precedence of those who dined in the
steward's room. Mr Perkins, the steward, sat at the head of
the table, Mrs Crambo at the foot; at Mr Perkins's right-
hand was Mrs Legg, Her Ladyship's maid, and at Mrs

Crambo's right sat Mr Fenton, the clerk of the stables. The clerk of the kitchen came next in importance, and then, in an order that length of service might determine, His Lordship's *valet-de-chambre*, the man-cook and the butler, the French confectioner — the bailiff and the Scotch gardener, when they came to town — and lowest in rank (perhaps because he had to snuff the candles) the groom of the chambers. In the servants' hall there was a far more numerous company, of footmen and chambermaids, a woman-cook, an under-butler, housemaids and grooms, over whom, in the Lowes-tofts' house, the vast figure of Stamford the coachman pre-sided. Here, too, there was rank and precedence — and at the foot of the scale a sort of *jacquerie* of boys and scullery-maids.

Having first learnt his place in this complex but orderly world, Moses was then taught how to improve it. He was a remarkably good-looking boy, and in his livery, of dark green coat with yellow facings and pale green breeches, he pre-sented a charming picture that greatly enhanced Mrs Crambo's dignity when she walked abroad with him in attendance — that increased her visible importance exactly as two footmen in the boot and another on the box with the coachman (all dressed alike) made obvious the Countess of Lowestoft's high degree — and Mrs Crambo, who had a real affection for Moses, was also sensible enough to realise that her position in the household might be substantially buttressed by a talented protégé.

He was clever as well as handsome, and listened attentively when she told him that the way to advancement required the art of reading, the faculty of penmanship, and the acquired talent of casting-up accounts. Reading, as it seemed, came to him by a light of nature — for penmanship she sent him, at her own expense, to a writing-school — and for account-ancy she pressed into her service a young man who was subordinate to the clerk of the kitchen.

To Mrs Crambo I, the direct descendant of Moses, owe an infinite gratitude. It was she who began to make him — under the careless good-will of the Countess — and having made the beginning of him was so wise as to push him, at the age of fifteen, into the vacant position of footman — junior of six — after having brought him to the notice of Mme Lebrun, Her Ladyship's new maid.

Mme Lebrun had the superlative art of so dressing a lady's hair as to compliment her and flatter fashion too; and, at the age of twenty-eight or thirty, an interest, almost devout, in the physical and social potentialities of handsome young men. — Never was Mrs Crambo's selfless regard for her foundling so purely demonstrated as in her suggestion, with Mr Perkins's approval, that Moses should be the footman who accompanied Mme Lebrun on her various errands about town; and rarely can a boy have profited more quickly, and more thoroughly, from such an association.

At eighteen — when Mme Lebrun left Her Ladyship's service to marry a substantial merchant in the City — Moses was frequently mistaken, by country visitors, for a young man of fashion; and the upper servants of the house, having overcome their initial jealousy of his advancement, now trusted him as one who would instinctively maintain the authority of rank and the principles of domestic hierarchy. He won their confidence in spite of wilful and eccentric ostentation.

It was the habit, in those days, for servants to exact vails from all who visited their master. Vails were tips; but tips as rigorously demanded as blackmail. When the visitor, having dined or supped, was about to leave, the servants of the house, from valet and butler down to the junior footman — and beyond him, the coachman, grooms, and yard-boys — would wait in double line for their fee; and heaven help the guest who was mean, or refused them. Now when Moses, taking his place in the line for the first time — and this was a

few weeks after he had been given the duty of escorting Mme
Lebrun on her errands — was offered the customary tip by
several departing visitors, all of whom were in a generous
mood, he staggered the complacency of his fellow-servants,
and excited the wonder of his master's guests, by bowing to
each in turn and refusing their vails with a civil but decisive,
'*Non, merci.*'

His fellow-servants, at first irate, were soon persuaded that
his idiosyncrasy, so far from harming them, enhanced the
distinction of Lord Lowestoft's hospitality, and would increase the number of his visitors. His Lordship was informed
of the peculiarity of his young footman, and re-discovered
the foundling whom he and his Countess had rescued after a
night at the theatre. The Countess — our dear Penelope —
had almost forgotten him: in the twenty years after her first,
so oddly delayed pregnancy, she was brought to bed of
fourteen children, nine of whom survived their infancy, and
with so much that demanded immediate attention, her dis-
regard of the periphery of her life must be excused; but when
she saw how handsomely her foundling had grown, and
heard him speak French — when she was told that he could
read and write and cast-up accounts — she was delighted
with the wisdom of her choice, and insisted that everything
should be done that might advance Moses in his career. —
Apprenticeship to a hairdresser, for instance.

A year or two later, when Lord Lowestoft resolved on a
tour through France and Italy, he took with him his old
friend Colley, the persistent letter-writer; his coachman
Stamford and his valet Mr Brass; and his promising young
footman Moses. In the course of their journey Mr Brass fell
ill of Italian cooking, and Moses was promoted to take his
place. He was confirmed in it when they returned to
London, and gradually, as Mr Perkins the steward grew
older, Moses assumed some of his tasks and responsibilities.

By the age of twenty-five he was exercising a good deal of authority in the house.

When he became His Lordship's valet he put away livery and dressed in much the same style as his master; in the identical style of the year before, indeed, for they were now of the same height and build, and there were those who said that an old coat looked better on Moses than ever it had on His Lordship. Mrs Crambo was outspoken in admiration, and the Earl and the Countess both made much of him. Ambition grew in him, and they, now openly proud of their foundling and unwilling to lose him, began to admit, though reluctantly, that his abilities were too evident to be confined for ever in private service.

It was Mrs Crambo who persuaded the Countess that he must be given the opportunity to advance himself, and Colley has left an account of a conversation in which Moses surprised them by a specific request. He knew exactly what he wanted, and that was His Lordship's influence to get him an appointment in the East India Company. According to Colley he spoke very well, stating his case frankly but modestly, and made it perfectly clear that he recognised the danger and uncertainty of life in India, but was ready to face them for the chance of surviving to make a fortune.

His Lordship was not easily persuaded that the choice was a wise one, and the Countess wept openly to think of Moses exposed to the danger of snakes and fevers and murderous Hindoos; but Moses was not to be deterred, and presently he got his way. In January, 1732, he boarded an Indiaman bound for the Hooghly with an appointment as Writer in John Company.

Throughout his service he wrote regularly, to Mrs Crambo until she died, and to both Lord and Lady Lowestoft. In 1906 his letters were collected, and privately printed, by my grandmother Lilian; who herself had lived and suffered in

India. They are dull reading, for he had no gift of description, and it is regrettably apparent that he was always more interested in his own prospects than in the people among whom he lived. He did eventually make a fortune, but he found it more difficult than he had expected, and for several years the burden of his narrative was fever and frustration. The way to make money was to engage in private trade, but for a junior writer this was almost impossible, and Moses complained angrily of restrictions that his seniors ignored but were binding on him. He survived fever and dysentery, however, and it was commonly accepted that if a young man could keep alive through three monsoons, he had no more to fear: and Moses, determined to come home a nabob or not at all, lived in Bengal for twelve years before the pagoda-tree was ripe for shaking — and then, in three more years, he made a fortune that gossip estimated at £120,000.

It may have been more than that, for when he did come home he bought land as other men bought wigs or waistcoats: an estate in Somerset, two neighbouring properties in Norfolk, a house in Arlington Street — that for a start. But a fortune stranger than great wealth was waiting for him, and at the age of forty-two — it was in 1747 he returned — he was immediately involved in high-pitched, gaudily romantic adventure, and in the course of it fell passionately and lastingly in love with a girl young enough to be his daughter.

As soon as he came to London he presented himself to his former patrons, and found all the household in a pitiable state of turmoil and distress. Lydia, the youngest daughter — the youngest of the children — had eloped with an Irish footman. Worse than that, she was married to him — married by a rascally parson in a tavern of the Fleet — and to heap gross indignity on stark ruin, it had now been discovered that the footman (Plunkett was his name) had furnished himself against the expenses of married life with three hundred guineas, stolen from what was thought to be a strong-box; with the Countess's *parure* of diamonds (ear-rings, necklace, bracelets and shoulder-knots); and with a small trunk full of flowered silks and Italian satins.

Lydia had left a letter in which she confessed her marriage, and begged forgiveness. Such love as hers, she said, if it were rightly understood, could not fail to find a pardon, for surely it had been born in heaven. 'But Plunkett', said the Earl, 'was born in an Irish bog, and nothing but a rope will shrive him.'

House-bound with gout, he sat with one hugely bandaged foot on a stool — sat hand-in-hand with his wife, and stroked her hand to soothe her. They were still a handsome pair, though shrunken a little with the years, and now her eyes were swollen with weeping. They had no one to help them in calamity. Colley was now bent and frail, and the oldest son had long since quarrelled with his father. The second had been killed at Fontenoy, and the third, still in the Army, was with Cumberland on the Maas; or somewhere near it. Only Henry, the youngest boy, was at home, and he, asthmatic from childhood, was too delicate to ride in search of the abductor.

The Countess appealed to Moses. 'Bring Lydia back to me,' she said, 'and I will forgive her as she begs me to. I will do anything to save her from the ruin of living with that bad Irishman. A thief as well as a seducer!'

'But where shall I look for them?' asked Moses — and got no help till he himself made enquiry of the servants. In Bengal, I suppose, he had had some experience of interrogation, and by questioning footmen and chambermaids separately — taking them one by one — he soon learnt more about Plunkett than his employers had ever known. He had not been born to household service, but had come to it in consequence of misfortune; and it was commonly believed, especially by the chambermaids, that he was a Jacobite and had been out in the rebellion of '45. (One of the footmen, however, said he had been a highwayman, and had taken service for concealment after killing a traveller on the Bath road.) Whatever the truth of it, he had created a romantic interest in the servants' hall — as well as in Lydia's innocent mind — and the chambermaid who knew most about him, and wept while she told her story, said he had a mother living in Wexford and he had often spoken of his intention to return there as soon as it was safe for him to travel.

Moses also discovered that the groom of the chambers, whose duty it was to lock the outer doors, had been out all night, in pursuit of pleasure, and had given his keys to Plunkett. He sent for the steward, reproved him for negligence, and told him to find out on what days and at what hour the stage-coach left for Bristol. It was then about two in the afternoon, and within a couple of hours the steward brought the news that a coach had left that morning, at six o'clock, with four passengers, all of whom were in middle life or older; but a private coach had been engaged by a young man, who might well be Plunkett, to go to Hounslow, which was the first stage on the west road.

I like to think of Moses, newly home from his long and comfortless years in Bengal — Moses with £120,000 in the bank — pressed immediately into police-work and service to his old employers, and I have often wondered if he was moved, not only by a sense of duty to his benefactors, but by sentiment: by a sentimental memory of Lydia as a child. She would have been about five or six when he went to India, and at that age she may well have been memorably pretty; for she grew into a young woman of exceptional beauty. He, as a servant, perhaps saw more of the children than their parents did, and it is not impossible that a tender image of the youngest of them lodged in his mind, and remained there,

bright-haired and ageless, while he lived in exile among a
dark and sullen people.

It is certain that he showed both enterprise and resolution
in his pursuit of the fugitives. It was manifest, he said, that
Plunkett would get out of the country as soon as he could —
not on Lydia's account, but to save his neck and sell the
diamonds he had stolen — and because England was still at
war with France his best chance of escape was from an Irish
port. He had a mother in Wexford — the girl Susan was
sure of that — and if he had a mother it was likely that he had
other friends and relations there. He would go to Wexford
if he could — Wexford for a start — and surely that meant
embarking at Bristol? The Irish wool-smugglers did much
of their marketing in Bristol — spending French money on
English goods; the Bristol market was as lawless as the Irish
coast — and there was sure to be a packet of some sort
loading there.

His Lordship found all this convincing, and gave orders
that his own coach should be made ready for a journey. It
would travel a little faster than the stage-coach, and if he
left at dawn the next day Moses was confident of over-taking
the fugitives, though they had twenty-four hours' start. In
that grim time of deeply rutted, miry roads, the stage-coach
took, I think, four days to reach Bristol; but its passengers
were given generous intervals at the posting inns — they
never hurried over their dinner, and they stopped well before
dark — so it was possible, by a reduction of comfort and a
happy avoidance of accident, to shorten the journey, and
Moses did indeed over-take the coach at Bath. But Lydia
and Plunkett were not in it. He had had two passengers of
their description, said the coachman, but they had travelled
with him only from Hounslow to Reading.

It was now Stamford, Lord Lowestoft's coachman, who
came to the rescue. He was a son of the old burly driver

whom Moses had known when he was in service, and his opinion was that anyone in a hurry would have had enough of the stage-coach by the time he reached Reading. 'Plunkett had money in his pocket,' he said. 'He's Irish, and he didn't willingly spend money — not his own money — but after looking over his shoulder all the way from Hounslow, you can depend on it he was growing impatient, and "Money be damned," he said, "I'll hire a coach for myself". There are two inns in Reading, both with a stable of good horses, where he could have found what he wanted.'

They drove on to Bristol: Moses and Stamford on the box, a groom in the boot, and in the coach, Susan the chambermaid. She had been taken to attend Lydia on the journey home — Moses was confident of rescuing her — and it may have occurred to him that Susan, who for reasons of her own wanted to see Plunkett again, might be useful in other ways.

They came to Bristol, and drove slowly along the quays. There were two or three ships from the West Indies unloading — but that trade had been diminished by fear of the French privateers — and at a farther quay two snows and a packet-brig. The brig was ready for sea, her hatches closed, some deck-cargo tidily disposed, and forward on the deck there was a little farewell-party going on: some women of the town drinking with the sailors and screaming with laughter at one who was dancing a jig. Yes, she was bound for Wexford, said a longshoreman — waiting only for the tide — but there was no sign aboard her of the passengers they were looking for. The skipper, said the longshoreman with a cock of his thumb, was in the tavern there.

The tavern on the quay had a dissolute, ramshackle look and was called *The Irish Harp*. 'Wait here,' said Moses to Stamford, and handed Susan from the coach. 'You will come with me.'

There were two men in the coffee-room, one of whom was,

roughly clad with little glinting eyes in a pug-nosed, long-lipped, leather-brown face — the other raven dark, brazenly handsome, wearing a long, pale-blue coat, yellow waistcoat, white breeches — and when Susan saw him she let out a great cry and ran forward, calling 'Tom! Oh, Tom!'

'A pox on you,' said Plunkett — and to Moses, 'And who are you, Sir?'

'A friend of Lord Lowestoft,' said Moses, 'and, for the present, his envoy.'

'Then a pox on you too, and damn you to hell into the bargain!'

From his long blue coat he pulled two pocket-pistols and fired point-blank at Moses. But the first mis-fired — how many lives were saved, in that century, by the failure of a flintlock? — and the Irish skipper, who on English soil had a superstitious fear of murder, knocked up his arm as he fired the second time — and Moses' hat went spinning from his head.

Then, from the deep pocket of his driving-coat, Moses fetched his own, long-barrelled pistol and with great delibera-tion pointing it at Plunkett's chest, fired. — And there, in that cold and purposive aim, is proof, I think, of his senti-mental motive: throughout his exile he had indeed remem-bered the fair-haired, youngest child of the family, and this was her seducer's proper punishment that he had intended from the beginning.

Susan, with a scream, flung herself on Plunkett's body, and now from all parts of the tavern and the streets outside came people running, some exclamatory, others shocked into silence — and on a dark stairway, white-faced under her yellow hair, stood Lydia. The others made way for her, and when she had seen that Plunkett was dead she walked, with a blind and stumbling movement, to a bench by the wall, and sat there crying quietly, as if crying for sheer tiredness.

Moses was about to go to her when someone, pulling Susan from Plunkett's body, roused the girl to a frenzy, and screaming hoarsely she ran, with blood on the lace at her breast, out of the tavern and across the quay — she hesitated for a moment, turned and saw Moses coming — and then, with a cry of defiance, jumped into the water.

Gaping and ox-eyed, a dozen idlers stood and watched her — the current took her down stream, but the air under her petticoats kept her afloat — and Moses, pulling off his driving-coat, plunged in and swam after her. He had no difficulty in saving her — there was a wherryman not far away — but then he had to stand for an hour in wet clothes, talking to a magistrate, making a formal statement, and by nightfall he was shivering with fever and delirious. The waters of the Avon were too cold for a servant of John Company.

It was Lydia who nursed him, and Susan, now much subdued, did as she was told and during two nights of burning fever and drenching sweats, changed his sheets while Lydia bathed his face. When he recovered his senses he lay for a long time, listening to their voices, before he spoke.

Plunkett was identified as a highwayman wanted for murder — if he had ever been a Jacobite, he had never done more for the cause than talking about it in taverns — and Moses received the thanks of the magistrates for ridding them of a notorious nuisance. The diamonds and the guineas were recovered, and during their homeward journey Lydia admitted that the happiness of her marriage had lasted two days only. Then she had discovered her mother's jewellery and her father's money in her own trunk, and Plunkett had told her that she must take the blame for theft if they were stopped and searched. He had done no more, he said, than provide her with a dowry — and without a dowry how could she have got a husband? He had laughed at her distress, and when she tried to run away from him, had beaten her with a cane.

There, then, is the romantic paragraph in the story of Moses; and it is illustrated by two miniatures that are among my dearest possessions. Both of them, on ivory, are by Peter Paul Lens, and that of Lydia is so enchanting — she is the very image of her mother at the same age — that Lens, not a very good artist, must have been inspired, by her, to paint as if he were a Cooper or a Cosway. The portrait of Moses is very different: he is like one of the grimmer English admirals, handsome enough, with noble eyes, but built of teak, not flesh and blood — and teak that had been aged by exposure to the weather for more than forty years. He shows every year of his age — and at forty-two he fell in love with all the passion and velocity of youth, and stayed in love, to find its fullness, with the stubborn persistence that had kept him in India to make a fortune.

He delivered the *parure* of diamonds, and Lydia, to her mother, the three hundred guineas to her father, and took coach again to Bristol. While he was there he had heard that a desirable estate in Somerset was in the market, and because he hated idleness, and wanted to establish himself in England, he went to see it; and having seen it, bought it. A month or two later he bought a house in Arlington Street, and called on William Pitt. He had developed a taste for politics, and the sort of politics he favoured was that established, for the Pitts, by Thomas (called 'Diamond') Pitt, who, somewhat earlier than Moses, had also carved a fortune from Bengal.

As so often happened, William Pitt was suffering from honesty, gout, and perplexity. Though he was Paymaster-General he refused to use the public funds for his own profit, and it was widely believed that he was already suffering from the mental instability that afflicted so many of his family. His gout was chronic, and now, in conjunction with his suspicion that honesty in high places was a mere eccentricity, it made him ill-humoured; and instead of welcoming Moses, he bade him be patient and wait a better opportunity for entering political life. A little while later Moses heard there was good land in Norfolk, and the more enterprising squires were improving their land; he went to inspect their work, discovered an agreeable estate that was for sale, and a lesser one that marched with it. He bought them both.

These activities occupied several months, and then, with his title-deeds in his pocket, he had a long conversation with Lady Lowestoft. His relief was as profound as hers had been when he learnt that Lydia's marriage would have no issue; and presently he proposed for her himself. Her Ladyship, overflowing with gratitude, was wholly in favour of the offer; His Lordship was doubtful. He remembered the origin of Moses, and though Her Ladyship thought it pretty and appropriate that *her* foundling should marry *her* daughter, His Lordship felt that a play-book and a basket would look out of place on his family-tree.

Moses admitted, without rancour, the handicap he suffered, but thought it might be obscured, if not removed, by his new possessions. His Lordship studied the title-deeds — invited another attack of gout with a third bottle of port — and came to the conclusion that Moses' argument was irrefutable. Lydia, pretending to be dutiful, meekly acquiesced; and later told him that even on her way to Bristol she had dreamt she was Andromeda, waiting for her Perseus, and had recognised him as soon as she saw him. I think it likely that she was as much in love with him as he with her.

They married, and for some years were so happy that Moses forgot his political ambitions — put off going to see

Pitt again — and when his sons were born (Edward in 1748, Charles two years later) he bought some more parcels of land, both in Somerset and Norfolk, to enlarge and round-off his estates, and make of them properties that would support with an adequate dignity the two branches of his family. He saw himself now, not only as a landed proprietor, but as the progenitor of landed gentry whose seed would carry his name into the ripening fields of English history; and his ambition swelled anew when he looked at his sleeping children and shifted some of its burden to their infant shoulders. Diamond Pitt had thrust his progeny into broad acres and the peerage, and so would he.

Lydia had settled down in Somerset in great content, and where she was contented, so Moses might have been; but for the boys' sake he revived his interest in politics and business — they went naturally together — and after renewing and enlarging his acquaintance with Pitt, whose pompous habit pleasantly reminded him of the Bengal nabobs, he was given the representation of a pocket borough and became a Member of Parliament at the general election of 1754.

As a parliamentarian he made no impression except by his unswerving loyalty to Pitt. He was too old to play an interested part in the personal feuds and ever-shifting family alliances of the House of Commons. On Pitt's behalf he disliked the King, and Newcastle, and Henry Fox; but he went no farther than that, and found more pleasure, and much more profit, in association with the great merchants of the City who already saw that England's destiny, and ever-deepening sources of wealth, lay oversea.

When war was renewed he shared the exultant patriotism that seemed to fill the country with a perpetual sunshine — for who could avoid exultation when a man was 'forced to ask every morning what victory there is, for fear of missing one'? — but though he rejoiced in the news of Clive's triumph at Plassey, Hawke's in Quiberon Bay, and the rose-crowned valour of our infantry at Minden, he heard with some misgiving that Wolfe had taken Quebec; for he, and others who could see a little farther than their noses, thought it was only fear of the French in Canada that kept the American colonists loyal — and if their fear was removed, their loyalty would vanish.

He grew ever more serious as he contemplated the world, and England's growing power in it. The fervour of his patriotism was edged with gloom and indignation when he contemplated the open and insidious enemies who abounded, not only beyond its shores, but within them — what had Fox done in the war but fleece the country to fill his own pockets? Frederick the Great took £700,000 a year from Pitt, and earned it — but how much had Fox taken, and what return had he made but mischief? When his pockets were full to overflowing, he spoke up for peace, and by corruption and chicanery got a majority for the Treaty of Paris, though Pitt, in an agony of gout, was carried into the House and spoke for three hours against it. Why would they not listen to Pitt?

In such a mood, Moses found increasing difficulties and the shadow of disappointment in his own family. Not that Lydia disappointed him — she, quite simply, was perfection formed in beauty — but the boys, Edward and Charles, often displeased him. Edward, though healthy enough, lacked spirit, and seemed to have no will of his own. He was a pretty boy — too pretty, with a girlish charm — and easily frightened. At Eton he made friends with Charles James Fox, the son of Pitt's iniquitous opponent, and that was a source of offence. But otherwise he gave little trouble. Perhaps too little. 'He looks like a girl, I think he should have been a girl,' said his father; but still hoped that age would improve him, give him gravity, manliness, and a sense of responsibility.

Charles, the younger boy, was different in all respects.

In his nonage he was fiery, rebellious, and intractable. He was thrashed almost daily, and grew harder and more indomitable with every beating. His father admired him — but would not admit his admiration — and was determined to make him obedient. He wanted to shape Charles in his own image, and till he was eleven or twelve Charles was equally resolved to shape himself to no one's liking but his own. But then the boy's temper changed. He listened gravely to what his father said, and showed a greedy appetite for his studies. Moses grew proud of him, boasted that his aptitude for Greek and Latin was equal to his horsemanship, and felt sure — or almost sure — that here was a son who would fulfil all his expectations. His doubt — his only doubt — was due to the boy's curiously withdrawn and secretive habit: a habit of mind, it seemed, as much as a habit of behaviour. He grew into a notable scholar, a fine shot, a daring horseman, and all this was just what Moses had wanted. But the more he conformed, the more he became a stranger in his father's house; and his father's pride in him was sometimes a little uneasy. Lydia was quite untroubled either by the weakness or the wilfulness of her sons; she was fond of them, in an easy, unthinking way, but love of her husband so dominated her life that her mind shrugged off all the imperfections of the world that lay beyond his shadow.

Presently his shadow was increased by the height of a coronet, for when Pitt went to the Upper House as Earl of Chatham, he took Moses with him as the Baron Storleyford of Storleyford in Somerset. Moses delighted in his new dignity, and half his pleasure was quite unselfish. To his dear Lydia, who had been born under a noble roof, he had now given her own title of nobility — she cried a little, wishing her father and her mother were still alive — and to make their new dignity more obvious Moses at once engaged an architect to improve the mansion-house in Somerset. It was a large and comely house, but of plain appearance — it was built in the reign of George I — and the wings that were now added, in a nice proportion, gave it grace as well as splendour.

Moses himself, about this time, was beginning to acquire a larger frontage. He was of medium height — a little more perhaps — with broad shoulders and a good carriage. When he first came home from India he had a gaunt and flattened look, but gradually he had put on weight and the healthy plumpness of his cheeks had long since mitigated the severity of his aspect. But now his well-fleshed body grew expansive, for he sat longer at table and took more pleasure from it. A good sirloin of beef was always his favourite dish, but that did not impair his appetite for boiled turkeys and oysters, or boiled fowls with bacon and oyster sauce — nor for great hams and well-fed geese — he had a liking for mince-pies and marrow puddings and a syllabub made of thick sweet cream and sifted sugar, sack and Rhine wine and lemon-rind — he ate with relish great wedges of Gloucester and Cheddar cheese — and he drank heartily of red port and white, with brandy and water for a cooling draught (he called it brandy-pani in memory of Bengal) and brandy punch after dinner. A heaviness about his neck and chin, the dull red of his cheeks, betrayed his hearty habit, but his strong shoulders supported with tolerable dignity his growing paunch. Lydia still thought him the handsomest man in England, and encouraged him to eat well and keep up his strength. But as he grew stouter, she grew strangely thin and pale.

For two or three years he found happiness in his title and his great house, but then the family was distraught and split by a quarrel that became too bitter for repair. It was Edward the elder son — the docile, girlish son — who was to blame, and his bad influence was Charles James Fox; their friendship at Eton had been renewed at Oxford, and with the stubbornness of a weakling Edward refused to break it off. At the age of twenty-one Fox became a junior Lord of the Admiralty, and in the great dispute about John Wilkes, and the right of the electors of Middlesex to choose their own representative, Fox took sides with those who declared that the House of Commons had an over-riding right: the right to exclude John Wilkes. And at his father's table, Edward, with hysterical tenacity, supported his friend Fox.

This was intolerable behaviour. Not only was Charles James Fox the son of Pitt's old thieving enemy — and therefore in the wrong from his conception — but now he too was opposing Pitt — yes, and laying an axe to the root of the tree of liberty. Pitt had said so! Pitt had come out of retirement, tired and frail but fighting still. Fighting for freedom — and John Wilkes. They said he was mad, but there was more sense in Pitt's madness than in the sanity of gravel-blind fools who at one moment clamoured for peace with Spain, and the next made war on Middlesex! No son of his, declared Moses, could march under their colours — or if he chose to, must leave his father's house for ever.

A bottle fell from the table. Edward, white of face, his voice tremulous, said his decision had been made, and he stood by Fox. Moses, empurpled by anger, threw a wineglass at him, and Edward, with blood trickling from his forehead, ran from the room. 'And that,' said Moses to his younger son, 'is the last I shall ever see of him.' The flame of anger went out, and gloom reduced it to a smouldering resentment. He reached for another glass, and filled it with a trembling hand. 'God has turned against me,' he said. 'A family divided against itself is the mark of God's displeasure. But what have I done? I have done nothing wrong. Nothing wrong!'

Lydia died six months later. She grew spectre-thin and pale, and the torment in her bowels became unbearable. But she complained only of the pain her husband felt, to see her suffer, and in the last full sentence she spoke, before agony became delirium, she told him yet again of her love.

Now Moses felt his world breaking beneath him. His hatred of Edward rose almost to the pitch of insanity, for by some obscure and twisted path of unreason he persuaded himself that Edward's treachery — to his father and to Pitt, to freedom and to England — had aggravated his mother's illness; and as he had foretold, he never saw his elder son again. The Norfolk estate was Edward's, entailed on him, and with a bitter contempt for his chance of enjoying it, Moses left him in possession. 'He will not prosper,' he said. 'God has turned against him and us.' *

His own life lay in ruins, and when he looked through dis-coloured eyes at the life of England, he saw that also reeling to collapse. On every side there was poverty and misrule, corruption and incompetence. During the fight for freedom, when Wilkes was its bawdy champion, there had been mob-law in London — sailors from the fleet had fought pitched battles in St James's Street — and who could contemplate the future without fear and dismay when he looked at the men who now were ruling England? There was near-anarchy in the American colonies, but instead of promising reform and using reason they were trying to coerce the colonists and tax them still — though they had no means of coercion but a navy crippled by corruption, and a diminished army whose dunder-headed generals would lead their troops to defeat with the precision of the parade-ground.

There was no comfort left in life but the comforts of the table; and now Moses ate and drank with a sullen relish as

* The present Lord Storleyford was prominent, in the 1930's, as one of Sir Oswald Mosley's supporters. He now lives in retirement. My branch of the family has had no communication with his, except of the most casual sort, for many years.

though the thick slices from the undercut of a sirloin of beef, or a boiled fowl in oyster sauce, a syllabub and another bottle of port, were trophies snatched from a losing battle. He ate heavily and drank deeply; but now his strong shoulders could no longer carry the great weight of his belly, and his once taut and commanding figure sank and grew slack, was changed and distorted into a caricature of human shape. His hard, decisive mind became an irrational and fearful organ, now craven, now absurdly belligerent; and over his third bottle he would ask, 'Without Charles, where would I be? But Charles may win all back. Charles may still redeem us.'

Charles was in the army now. He had put his scholarship behind him, and told his father that he intended, in due course, to go into parliament. To qualify for high office he thought the experience of military service would be useful: to a knowledge of ancient history he proposed to add a practical knowledge of modern war, and thus equipped he would look for speedy advancement. — All this he explained clearly and without emotion: he showed a cold assurance of his ability, his planned and measured ambition, that rejoiced his father's heart. Charles had put away at last his long habit of secrecy, and revealed himself as the very son for whom he had always hoped. — Let Edward shrivel in the east winds of Norfolk! The Somerset estate would be Charles's, and the house with its fine new wings would be a proper seat for his greatness. Charles would be his justification — his pride if he should live to see him installed in greatness — and if death came first, he could die happy in the knowledge that Charles would write an epitaph of glory for his name.

Moses bought for Charles a cornet's commission in the 2nd Life Guards of Horse, and when war with America was imminent exchanged it, with the expense of a little more money, for a captaincy in the 5th of Foot. Charles embarked for America in January, 1775, and after he had sailed Moses began to realise, or to admit, that the education of war could be dangerous. He was not one of the fools — and they were many — who expected the colonists to throw down their arms and run as soon as they saw a column of regulars marching against them.

For Moses the months went slowly. He was living now in his house in Arlington Street, and to him the greenery of spring seemed garish and interminable. Summer came at last, and with it the news that an attack on Boston had cost us heavy losses. He waited still, not often sober, for a despatch that would name the dead, and when it came, with Charles's name on it, he fell into an abyss where fury contended with stark despair.

All he had lived for — served and struggled and fought for — all he had achieved and gloried in had been destroyed and turned to ashes. Lydia was dead before her time — Lydia his love was dead — and their elder son was a traitor to his father's faith, banished and not to be thought of without shame. His leader, great Pitt, was a fugitive from rancour and bad men's unbelief—and what was there to live for now?

Charles was dead. Dead on Bunker Hill, killed by a rabble of the furious colonists. Charles, his last hope, had gone.

Curse God. Curses and damnation fall on God the first progenitor. — Another bottle of port, and the pulse in his brow beat more heavily. He felt a nagging pain behind his brow. There was doom at home as well as abroad, but he would die as he had lived. He would die hard. — He called for his valet and his steward, and said to the valet, 'Put me to bed.' But to the steward he said, 'Open the cellar, and let all the servants take what they want. Let them drink it dry, for there's nothing in it I shall want to-morrow.'

He lay in his bed, the quilt a little mountain over his belly, and as the din and uproar of a horde of drunken servants mounted and rose from the floor below, he cursed his Maker in the heights and in the depths, from the dawn of eternity to its ultimate dusk. He pulled himself up, climbing to the pillows with the labour of a mountaineer, and poured a last goblet of brandy. A good brandy from Nantes. He let the bottle fall, but drank what he had poured, and with a whispered valediction of damnation to his God, he died.

IX Rise and Shine!

THAT was how it all began. There, in that old ruffian,
was the tap-root of my family-tree. He was the first of us
Vanbrughs, and though his name was a mere fiction, it was
none the worse for that. For we are all, in a sense, no more
and no better than fictions. Mere paragraphs or sentences —
some less than that, only a broken phrase or a vocable crying
from the dark — in the vast, tragico-romantico-comico-
bawdy novel that God began to write before there was paper
to write on, and still is writing when all the forests of the
world are being felled to make paper for the novelettes that
so many of His faithful apes are writing.

And now — now — do you see the change of temper in me?
In the dark hour of my despair, reeling in the vertigo of an
oceanic hangover, I could find no straw to cling to — God
had vanished, God was not — but God returned when I
began to think of my father, and beyond him of my life's long

provenance. Belief came back as I rehearsed the troubled
tale of my ancestry because — though patched like a cottage-
quilt with farce, futility, and gross ineptitude — it was a tale
so stiff and stubborn with intent to live, to propagate and
persist. A patch-work quilt of folly and fatuity and a brutal
appetite for life: of temperance and intemperance, neither
much better than the other: of faith and despair, neither
enduring: of love like sunshot, pricking showers in April
(there must have been that) and the withered herbage of
parched and barren years: of great meals, oysters and turtle
soup, partridges and venison and ruby-dripping sirloins, with
beer in the barrel and cellars full of wine — and shrivelled
lips dribbling their gruel: of health and sickness, labour-
pains, and death-beds as reluctant as a never-opened pelvis
to let out the soul: of little piddling desires, trumpery little
men and their cackling little women, and the drum-
thumping, purple-canopied history they composed....

Yes, I was feeling much better. My hangover had gone —
as a matter of interest, I know the recipe for that and never
suffer more than an hour or two. I take, in the first place, a
raw egg beaten up in a glass of brandy with some Worcester
sauce and a dash or two of tabasco, a sprinkling of angostura
bitters. Then a good breakfast, however much the prospect
nauseates: bacon and eggs and a pot of black coffee. An hour
or two later I feel quite well again — sometimes really brisk
and well — and this particular morning my bilious inertia
suddenly gave way to an almost vulgar sensation of well-
being. For that, of course, neither Worcester sauce nor
bacon-and-eggs were primarily responsible: it was my
re-awakened faith in God that did it.

Old Moses Vanbrugh, cursing God on his drunken death-
bed — cursing God for the loss of a son and a pain in his
head because there was no one else he could curse except
himself, and none of us willingly does that — Old Moses had

rightly found, for his blasphemous abuse, his true progenitor. There was no shadow on Moses' faith, and none on
mine. It was God who had stitched and shaped the patch-
work quilt: if you look at it, study it, and ponder its pattern
and constituents, you may say 'All is monstrous and meaning-
less,' but you cannot deny it was *made*. The pieces did not
fall into place by accident, but were designed and assembled
for a purpose known to Him though inscrutable to us.

This rejoicing thought — this deduction, this insistent conclusion — brought me back to a sharper consideration of
myself. To begin with, I studied my appearance in the once
good though now rather darkly spotted cheval mirror for
which, perhaps unwisely, I had paid £2.10s. And my reflexion reassured me. I still made a good figure. So good
that a thought recurred of my youthful ambition to become
a prince of the Church: how well the robes and majesty of
a bishopric would have suited me! With what dignity,
in my brocades and stiffened satins, I could have prayed,
preached, blessed, or thundered my pious denunciation of
the world!

But I was too old now to think seriously of that, and
because of my enveloping and profound euphoria I passed
easily — with a murmured *Simply the thing I am shall make me
live* — to the other evaluation of my abilities; and in the
spotted mirror I saw myself in the alternative dignity of the
Perfect Butler. I was so light of heart, for a moment, that I
laughed aloud as in imagination I heard my rich employer
call 'Vanbrugh!', and saw myself turn and bow slightly to
his request with a dignity far beyond his compass. If I could
find a household wealthy enough to employ me, there
would be little doubt, after a twelvemonth, as to who was
master in it.

But of imagination, that's enough. Facts must be admitted
before imagination is entertained — and the dominating fact

was that I had recovered both health and faith. Parolles had washed and shaved, and was ready for the next chapter.

I made some pretence to dress the main window, and found a place for the Empire mirror that I had repaired with Seccotine. I shifted a few chairs, moved the stuffed alligator to a darker corner, and stacked more tidily on their shelf the hundred-odd volumes of the *Annual Register*.... But where, I wondered, was my escape-hatch?

What was I to do? And where should I go? For clearly I had had enough of Melbury. It was clear, too, that my poor wife — my once dear Olive, burdened as she was with two christened children, and within her the growing promise of another — could not come with me. But I would leave her without disquiet of conscience, for she and her mother lived close as cauliflowers in a gardened row, leaning their pale hearts together, and old Trumbull of Trumbull, Tranter and Payne was a warm man well able to look after her and his grandchildren: close, mean, and grudging to me, he would be generous enough to them. And so, without remorse or fear for their future, I could say goodbye to them. Or better, leave them quietly, without a spoken goodbye, which would only start a painful, quite useless, and probably tear-stained argument.

A silent farewell, a moonlight flitting: that must certainly be my general plan. Common-sense dictated it, and so did my sense of pity for poor Olive. But what then? Where should I go, and what should be my goal? I had a feeling — it had been growing for some years — that this sceptred isle was too small for me: this blessed plot, this earth of Mars, this England, had become, for me, no better than a sub-urban allotment where pale mechanics grew shrivelled vegetables on their misused Sunday mornings — no place for me, and no earth of Mars in these days of pampered youth and a populace living in a cocoon of petty restrictions and comfort on the instalment plan. England was too small and dimly lit: that was its disability, and in some degree the reason for my present plight. I would not leave it without regret, but leave it I must: I owed that to myself.

The shop-door opened, with the double peal of its warning bell; but it was not a customer who came in. It was Edna, still in the blue denim trousers and the woollen body-garment of nigger pink that I had seen with such dislike from my bath-room window: her hair tied in a duster, a cigarette between her lips.

'Nice weather for ducks, isn't it?' she said.

'It has stopped raining, and the sun is coming out,' I answered — with, I fancy, a touch of cold annoyance in my voice.

'I got my feet wet, just crossing the road — look!'

She cocked up her left foot, balancing on the other leg, and showed me a sodden, cracked, and broken sole.

'If you wear shoes like that,' I said, 'you deserve any discomfort that's going.'

'So that's the mood you're in?'

'I've told you before...'

'You don't like me in trousers, and pink doesn't suit your complexion. Yes, I know! But I like comfort.'

She dropped her cigarette and crushed it on the floor. She sat on a corner of my desk and said, 'I saw Olive and the kids going out, so I thought you'd be all alone and might want cheering up a bit.'

'You mustn't be seen coming in here...'

'I can be a customer, can't I? Suppose I want to buy that stuffed alligator? It'd be as much fun as you, when you're in a mood like this.'

She got up, took a step towards me, threw her arms round my neck, and with her mouth an inch from mine said fiercely, 'Pompous old bugger, aren't you?' Then, opening her warm

231

lips, pressed them close in a long, demanding kiss, and I, incapable of denial, felt my anger changing shape, changing its intention, and my shallow impulse to rebuff and humiliate her found a deeper purpose in a sudden desire to show my mastery and prove it by possessing her. We kissed, long and closely, till I felt her weight on my arms, hanging in submission, and pulling her behind a partition that half-divided the shop — a partition lined with book-shelves and the Complete Works of Ruskin in green morocco — I threw her down in semi-darkness on a pile of dusty carpets. I remember the bitter smell of dust in my nose, and the rough surface of a folded Axminster, and as I pulled apart the revolting pink cardigan she wore, a loose button broke from her blouse and like a sponge-diver breaking the bright surface of the Ionian sea her right breast leapt to my lips and eyes. — And then, with a double peal, the shop-door rang its warning bell.

Justly, I think, I pride myself on the speed and dexterity with which I recovered from an awkward position and a situation potentially embarrassing. I did not make the mistake of pretending I was alone. I transferred my interest from Edna to the carpets, and slowly rising, as if from inspection of their condition, I said, loudly and clearly, 'They all need cleaning: the three Axminsters and the two big Wiltons. Yes, and the Shiraz rug as well. Get them done right away.' — And to Edna I whispered, 'Don't show yourself. Go through the house and out by the back door. Quickly now.'

Then, brushing my hands, I walked round to face my customers — a man and his wife, whom at first glance I recognised as Americans of the better sort — and with the amiable deference of which I am consummately a master — it is simple honesty that compels the admission, and false modesty must not stand in its way — I said to them, 'Forgive me for having kept you waiting. There's nothing more tiresome in my trade than disposing of second-hand domestic carpets; but I can't afford to quarrel with my bread-and-butter, so I have to put up with it.'

She was larger than her husband, both taller and broader, but he had a carriage and a countenance that clearly showed a habit of authority; and for a moment I could not decide which of them to address.

Then the lady asked, 'Did I hear you speak of a rug from Shiraz?'

Quickly I answered, 'Of inferior quality and in poor condition.' — I went into the backward part of the shop to make sure that Edna had gone, and taken the rug — which had no more connexion with Shiraz than I have, but it was the smallest there and she may have used it to cover her dishevelment — and returning, said, 'My assistant has taken it to be cleaned, but in any case it was not the sort of rug I would show to a serious customer.'

'How do you know I am serious?' she asked.

'In my business,' I said smoothly, 'one is bound to learn a little practical psychology.'

The severity of her expression was beginning to relax, when her husband interposed his question. 'Those two Chinese horses in your window,' he said, 'what are they?'

'T'ang,' I said.

'Genuine?'

'To the best of my belief, yes.'

'Can I have a look at them?'

'But certainly.'

I fetched them from the window, and put them on a small table. He sat down and studied them closely.

'Have you any good Oriental rugs?' asked his wife.

'Unfortunately, no. A week ago I had a very fine Bakhtiari, a garden carpet — but since then, nothing of any value. I am so sorry.'

'Tell me something more about these horses,' said her husband.

'It's a very nice pair. If they were real — I mean, living horses — I think you'd say they show their breeding very clearly; and have, perhaps, rather more spirit than many I've seen. And the colour is pure.'

'Where did they come from? What's their provenance?'

He stood up and looked me straight in the eye with a glance that was perhaps too consciously — or perhaps only habitually — 'searching'. He had attractive eyes: pale grey, bright, set wide apart in a handsome, tight-lipped, muscular square face. A man in his early fifties, dressed in conventional dark clothes: not London tailoring, but good New York. I am no expert at distinguishing American accents, but his was of the sort that one associates, instinctively, I suppose, with Groton and Harvard.

I smiled — a professional smile, that politely deprecated his question — and made a small, restrained movement of my hands, as if to put it away from both of us. I was trying hard to think of a good answer.

'It's sometimes a little difficult to speak of provenance. One has to consider one's clients: the clients who have parted, perhaps reluctantly, with their treasures.'

Saying nothing, still holding me with his steady gaze, he began, impatiently, to pat his pockets: feeling for something, looking-by-touch for something he wanted.

'Here it is,' said his wife, and from a large black handbag produced a heavy silver cigar-case. He took a cigar, without thanking her, and deftly removing the band, pierced it with a small gold instrument that he found in a waistcoat pocket, and lighted it. This performance deeply impressed me. It was so unlike the common American pattern in which the husband, decently deferential if not actually in attendance, is trained to fetch and carry for his wife. He, on the contrary,

234

accepted her services, took them easily and naturally; and she, remember, was a handsome woman, bigger than he, dressed and corseted with a stern aversion from display and absolute indifference to expense.

I made a sudden resolution; or, to be more accurate, I was suddenly visited by inspiration. I laughed — a light, embarrassed laugh — and said, 'You are compelling me, sir, to be autobiographical. To explain how these horses came into my possession...'

'That's what I want to know,' he said.

'Then, sir, I must tell you that until six years ago I was butler to the late Earl of Lowestoft; and although, in his will, he had already left me a substantial legacy, he insisted, on his death-bed, on presenting me with these T'ang horses as a personal gift in recognition of what His Lordship was pleased to call "the great distinction" of my service to him.'

'The Earl of Lowestoft?' said the lady, and looked at the horses with more interest than she had previously displayed.

'And you were his butler?' asked her husband.

'From 1945, when I was released from service with the Royal Air Force, till 1951, when His Lordship died. Before that — from 1936 till 1939 — I had been His Lordship's valet.'

'Emily,' said my customer, turning to his wife, 'this is *it*.'

'It certainly looks that way,' she answered.

'But first things first,' he said. 'Now about these horses: you say they were part of Lord Lowestoft's collection...'

'No, sir. That is to exaggerate His Lordship's interest in *chinoiserie*. His Lordship had, of course, a treasury — a veritable treasury — of pictures, furniture, mediaeval armour, *objets d'art*, and tapestries. But it would be going too far to say that he ever collected Chinese paintings or sculpture. He had some very good pieces, which he had acquired almost by accident...'

'A very fortunate accident.'

'So it turned out; though it was, of course, quite unfore-
seen when His Lordship, as a very young man, joined the
international force that advanced on Pekin...'

'When was that?'

'At the time of the Boxer rising: was it 1899 or 1900?
Not that it matters, does it? What happened, sir, was that
His Lordship, like many other young men who go abroad,
was eager to acquire souvenirs of his visit to Pekin, and these
horses, with some other pieces, were, in fact — and I must
trust your discretion when I tell you this — they were, to put
it crudely, loot from the Summer Palace.'

My customer, with a loud and sudden laugh — a curiously
young laugh for so mature a man — patted my pale horses on
their round buttocks and said, 'Loot from the Summer
Palace, eh? Well, that's a good enough provenance for me.
Yes, sir. And now tell me what's the price.'

From a drawer in the little table on which the horses
pranced I took a catalogue and pointed to an item I had
marked. 'This was a sale at Christie's a few months ago —
no, not that lot. That was a pair of Wei Dynasty horses that
made 480 guineas, and should have made more, I thought.
But this item, sir: a tomb figure horse of the T'ang Dynasty,
175 guineas. Now these that you are buying are far superior
— superior in every way — and for the pair of them I could
not ask less than...'

'Don't say it in guineas,' he said. 'I can't work out what
guineas mean in real money.'

Hurriedly I thought again, and firmly but gently said,
'Four hundred and fifty pounds, sir.'

'Would you knock off the fifty?'

'If I were to do so, I would be haunted by the thought of
coming face to face with His Lordship, in Heaven, and
having to admit that I had so undervalued his gift.'

'I'm an Episcopalian myself,' said my customer, 'and with

that provenance — well, I guess it's fair enough.' From an inner pocket he fetched a book of the American Express Company's Travellers' Cheques that looked to me as thick — oh, as thick as a Prayer Book — and sat down to do a little sum. 'If you'll come with me to the nearest bank, I'll pay you right away,' he said.

His wife said, 'I suppose Lord Lowestoft kept a considerable establishment?'

Here I was on safe ground; or relatively safe. For his youngest son had been at my college at Cambridge, and twice I had stayed at Norcutt Hall, unenviable weeks under a ponderous discipline in circumstances of cut-cost, Spartan discomfort. But I made a good story of it, and Mrs Kenyon — that, I now learnt, was her name — listened with a lively, close attention. So, I could see — while he was translating dollars into pounds — did Mr Kenyon.

'Do you make a good living out of this business?' he asked; and with an accountant's look in his eyes he traversed, in dubious scrutiny, the diminished contents of my shop. Mentally I tossed a coin for Yes or No; and it came down *No*.

'Far from it,' I said.

'How's that?'

I pretended a moment's reluctance, and then, with the rueful smile of an honest man acknowledging defeat, I said, 'I'm afraid I'm no match for the dealers, sir. I thought, because I had lived so long in a house where every chair, every picture, every piece of glass or silver was of value, that I was well trained for such a business as this. And so, in a way, I was. I know good from bad, the genuine article from the spurious. That knowledge has become a sort of instinct. But you need more than knowledge to compete with the dealers, the real professionals in the business. You need capital, and I had very little. You need the goodwill and association of a ring of dealers, and I found myself incapable, sir, of stooping to their methods and accepting their practices. I was brought up on stricter principles.'

'Are the antique dealers in England dishonest?' asked Mrs Kenyon.

'I wouldn't say that,' I replied, 'but there are degrees of honesty, and — oh, perhaps I had set myself too high a standard.'

I got up, and crossing to the door looked out at a watery, pretty view. A thin sun was shining on wet pavements and the puddled gutters; and my shoulders, I hoped, looked like the back of a good man bowed, but not broken, by angry circumstance. I could hear the Kenyons talking quietly to each other, and then he asked another question. I had, by then, decided on the line I was going to take. It was a gamble, but my only hope lay in gambling.

'What are you going to do?' asked Kenyon. 'Are you going to hang on, hoping things may improve, or do you mean to make a change?'

'You, sir,' I said, 'have just bought the last two pieces of any value that I have. The other things here — a hundred pounds would buy them all. But with your money I can pay off a few small debts, and now I'm free to accept an offer I was made, only the other day, for the house itself. It's mortgaged, of course, but if I sell it — and that, now, is what I shall do — I'll be able to start again, free of debt, and thanks to you with two or three hundred pounds in my pocket.'

'And what's in your mind for your next venture?'

'My mind is open — wide open — to any suggestion,' I said.

'Have you never thought of going back to your old job? I should think a highly trained and experienced butler could always find employment.'

'In this country? In England to-day, sir? You don't

realise how things have changed from what I was used to! Except for the Royal palaces and one or two ducal houses — and even they, how shrunken, how belittled and middle-class they are! Do you know, sir, that in all England there is hardly a house in which you will find a groom of the chambers and a clerk of the kitchen? And with my background, with my experience, how could I be satisfied with employment in some impoverished castle where I would have no staff — no adequate staff — nothing but a few ill-trained women and perhaps some refugees from central Europe — to maintain the order I'm accustomed to? No, Mr Kenyon, I have no hope whatever of finding the sort of employment I should require: not in England.'

'England's not the only country in the world: not nowadays,' said Mr Kenyon; and of his wife enquired, 'Do you still want to see the Abbey?'

'I certainly do.'

'I can cash these cheques in any of your banks, but I'm used to dealing with Lloyd's. Have you got a branch of Lloyd's Bank here in Melbury?'

'It's in Market Street,' I said.

'Then let you and me walk round to the bank while Mrs Kenyon takes the car and goes to see the Abbey.'

'The Abbey is barely a hundred yards from here.'

'Mrs Kenyon doesn't like walking, not even a hundred yards.'

We went out, and a well-taught chauffeur, with doffed cap, opened the door of the hired Daimler. Mrs Kenyon got in, and Kenyon and I, very slowly, walked towards Market Street.

'I'm a lawyer in New York,' he said, 'but not the sort of lawyer that handles crime. We just handle the source of crime, or the impetus to crime: property, real estate, big money.'

He looked at me with a dry, Yankee assessment to see how I would take that; and with a response of genuine liking I bowed slightly, in acknowledgment of his joke, and smiled with the proper degree of understanding.

Then he told me that one of his most important clients, who was also a personal friend, was a Mr T., who owned a large part of Texas from whose kindly soil petroleum came gushing like milk from a terrestrial udder. To say that Mr T. was rich meant nothing unless you knew something about Texas and how riches were measured there. Mr T. was rich even by Texas standards, and by Texas standards the Maharajahs of our old Indian Empire had been younger sons ploughing a shallow furrow of enjoyment on a boy's allowance. But Mr T. had come up the hard way: he hadn't been born to riches, he had made them for himself, and he was still uncertain about the domestic management of great wealth.

'But when I say that,' said Mr Kenyon, 'don't misunderstand me or under-rate him. He's a very great man with an imaginative mind, a driving energy, a sense of know-how in his own field that's little short of genius, and natural good taste. He just lacks the intimate, day to day knowledge of how to run a household that's got too big for easy handling, though it still isn't big enough for his requirements. And what he wants...'

At this moment we arrived at the bank, and I, in a ferment of anticipation, had the nervous happiness of introducing Mr Kenyon to the manager. Mr Wotherspoon had treated me as generously as he could, and I was very pleased to give him the happiness of talking to a rich American. He was a man with a curiously shaped head, it was thin, bald, and narrowed to a perceptible ridge. He was a good golfer, and the most expert coarse-fisherman in the county. He was, of course, delighted to help Mr Kenyon, and while he checked the translation of dollars into pounds, Mr Kenyon said to me, 'It's something more than a butler that he wants. I think you could rightly say it's a major-domo — and he's prepared to pay a handsome salary to the proper man.'

I felt as if the walls of the bank — the glass and stone and polished mahogany of my immediate environment — were dissolving in a sudden draught of sunshine, to leave me, alone, on an eminence of blissful achievement and absolute, calm power. True, I could not see the landscape of my domain, for I knew nothing of Texas; but as if to remedy my ignorance, Mr Kenyon said, 'Here are some photographs of his place.'

White arches in the sun. Colonnades. A fountain in a courtyard: a patio, I should say. Buildings in the Spanish Mission style: how thankful I was that he had not hired a modern architect! — And everything enormous: stables for forty, at least. And on his airfield a large machine with four engines, a couple with twin engines, and a small flock of Austers, Pipers, or lightweights of that sort.

I made an effort to control my emotion, and without a tremor in my voice I said, 'How very interesting to see the Texan way of life.'

We walked back to my shop — my inside pocket murmurous with the whispering of £5 notes — and Mr Kenyon said tentatively, 'It just occurred to me, as a possibility, that the idea of living in Texas, in that sort of highly privileged employment, might attract you. The salary would be something in the nature of...'

It was more than the Bishop of Winchester gets; and though it would mean, of course, my forfeiting for ever the dream of signing an episcopal letter *Gratiano Winton:*, or *Gratiano Bath: et Well: —* well, why repine? I had really abandoned that hope long ago.

'I must think it over,' I said.

'I don't want to intrude into your private life,' said Mr Kenyon, 'but may I enquire if you have strong domestic ties? Have you a family?'

'My married life,' I said, 'had no greater success than my career in business — and, I daresay, for the same reason. I set, perhaps, too high a standard. And I am, in consequence, almost alone in the world. I have no ties whatever.'

'In that case, if you did decide to accept this position, you could come pretty soon?'

'But surely, under your immigration laws, it takes months to get permission to enter the United States with a view to permanent employment?'

'Not if I'm there to help you,' said Mr Kenyon. 'I don't want to boast, but I have a certain amount of influence at our Embassy in London, and a good deal more in Washington.'

'It is,' I said thoughtfully, 'a temptation.'

Outside my shop, opposite the chemist's that my *devadasi* patronised and in full view of half the windows of Mrs Buttermere's Family Hotel, Mr Kenyon stopped and spoke with a new urgency.

'Before I left New York,' he said, 'I promised my friend Mr T. that I would find in England a major-domo who would serve him faithfully, who would manage his domestic establishment on the traditional lines of an English noble household, and of whom he could be proud. Well, I went to all the big London agencies, and what did I find? A bunch of handsome old cripples who might have served his purpose forty years ago, and a queue of pale-faced pansies with voices like something coming out of a leaky pipe. Well, they're no use to him. And I was in despair, because I'd pledged my word, not only to find him a major-domo who would be a major-domo, but to bring him back with me.

And Mrs Kenyon and I — this is Tuesday — are flying to
New York on Friday....'

It was, I suppose, an hour later — perhaps an hour and a
half — when Edna, soft-footed, came into our shabby little
sitting-room behind the shop, and suddenly startled me by
reading aloud, over my shoulder, the letter I was, with some
difficulty, writing to my wife.

' "My dear Olive," ' she declaimed, ' "I have just been
given a remarkable opportunity to bring off a very profitable
deal. It is much bigger business than anything I have done
for a long time, and I cannot afford to ignore it. It means,
however, that I shall be away from home for three or four
days, and I have to leave at once..." '

That was as much as I had written, and now Edna — who
had taken me completely by surprise — leaned over me, her
hands on my upper arms (her nails were dirty) and her left
breast softly boring into my right shoulder-blade, her breath
warm on my cheek — and then, with her hoydenish familiarity that has often irritated me, she ruffled my hair and
brusquely demanded, 'Well, what are you going to say next?
Going to tell her that I'm coming with you? And where are
we going?'

She pulled me away from the table — chair and all — and
plumply sat herself down on my lap. She kissed me warm
and fondly, with demanding lips, and her breasts, impor-
tunate, nuzzled my chest. I could feel her body coming to
life, as it always did when she was in the mood for love-
making. Indeed I have sometimes thought that she regarded
love as a sort of superior gymnasium in which all her
remarkable muscles could take their exercise.

But suddenly her mood changed, she sat up, brisk and
business-like, and said, 'Well, where is it? Where are we
going? Come on now! You said the other night we'd have to

243

have a few days off on our own, a few days together without all the old bitches in Melbury spying on us — and God knows we've got plenty to say! Well, this is our chance, isn't it?'

'Now look here,' I said, 'we must be sensible about this...'

'That's what I'm saying,' she answered, and took from the table an auctioneer's advertisement of a sale of furniture, pictures, and *objets d'art* at Llanbwlchy Manor, Llancwmbwlch, Carmarthenshire. 'But think of me asking my way to a place with a name like that! I'd get lockjaw first.'

I had, in fact, decided to tell Olive that I was going to Llanbwlchy Manor to buy, on commission, a notable collection of Chinese porcelain. She would, I knew, soon learn that I had had important-looking visitors — manifestly rich Americans — and she would quickly notice that my two pale horses had gone. Therefore my American customers were amateurs of *chinoiserie*, and the Llanbwlchy collection was well known. It seemed the perfect excuse for a sudden departure: having sold them a pair of T'ang horses, and shown myself knowledgeable of such things, my Americans had asked me to be their agent and buy for them some *famille verte* vases, K'ang-Hsi bowls, and such-like pretty things — what more natural? But I had not expected Edna's arrival and her quickness in jumping to a conclusion. I felt uneasily that unless I took very good care I should find myself, within the next day or two, in her possessive arms in some hole of an inn in the depths of Carmarthenshire; where, of course, I had no intention of going. I meant to give Olive a sound and convincing reason for believing that I was on my way to Llancwmbwlch — and then I proposed to take the first train to London.

Edna bit my right ear — a habit of hers which I always disliked — and asked, 'Do you think they sleep in beds in Wales? So long as there's a decent bed, I don't mind what the place is called. When do we start?'

It was the bite, I think — so wanton, so unprovoked — that persuaded me I must be ruthless with her. Fresh in my mind was the fact that I had told Kenyon I was a man without ties, alone in the world; and so, in truth, I felt myself to be. I had told myself — though it was bitter news — that I must sacrifice my loved and loving Edna to my new career. She would be an intolerable handicap if I took her with me, and though to leave her behind would strip the coating of my heart, it was the price I had to pay. Poor Edna! But among the photographs which Kenyon had shown me was a picture of some of the women servants at Mr T.'s great house. They made a pretty group, smartly dressed, and in their dark, Mexican way some of the girls were strikingly handsome. Edna, I realised, would never get on with them. She would not be happy in Texas.

So now — my ear was still smarting — I said to her, 'We can't possibly go together to Llancwmbwlch. You see that, don't you? But if you really want to come...'

'Don't you want me to?'

I kissed her. I patted her thigh, I made the appropriate vocal noises and said, 'Surely this is the best plan: that I go this afternoon, and find a decent room for you. Then, when you come to-morrow, I'll meet you. The contents of the house are open to view for two days, and the sale may last another two. So we'll have three or four nights together.'

'What's the fare?' she asked. 'I'm broke — and I want a new dressing-gown. Something decent.'

I put a hand in my inside pocket and felt the comfortable wad of £5 notes: they were the last of the old sort, the lovely, tissue-thin, rustling, big white notes, and with delicate fingers I detached two from the rich thickness of my windfall.

'You can do better than that,' she said. 'They were Americans, weren't they? And they bought those two Chinese horses. Oh, I've been watching you! And you always said those horses were valuable — so you can do a lot better than ten quid.'

After some argument I gave her another £15, but I was so annoyed by the mercenary temper she showed that I really felt no compunction — or very little — at the thought of her fruitless visit to Llancwmbwlch, and her anger when she arrived. We parted, however, on affectionate terms — indeed, I kissed her goodbye with the most genuine warmth and real regret — and with a sudden access of confidence I finished my letter to Olive.

Dear Olive! I felt almost fond of her as I realised that I should not see her again; and it was a great relief to know that as the house and business were in her name — a year or two ago I had raised some money by the transfer — I had no need to bother about selling them.

I had already packed a couple of suitcases, and ordered a taxi. I drove to the station and took a local train to Swindon. It would be idle to pretend that I felt no pang of sorrow as I left Melbury behind me, for my mother was buried there, and so were my youth and all the hopes of youth; but to give way to sorrow would have been stark folly, for now, at thirty-eight — was I so old? It seemed impossible — now the hopes of youth were miraculously revived, and the prospect of America was like the prospect of rapture-and-champagne that preceded (with, I must admit, a too extravagant optimism) my first love affair — and how long ago was that?

At Swindon I made enquiry about the trains to Llancwmbwlch — to leave evidence of my intention, if evidence should be sought — and twenty minutes later unobtrusively boarded the Paddington express. I arrived in London with a quite extraordinary sense of enlargement, and slept in a small hotel in Bayswater that was managed by an old friend of my years in the Royal Air Force.

Mr Kenyon proved as good as his word, and within twenty-four hours I had my American visa, and the comforting addition of five hundred dollars to cover incidental expenses. But also — and this caused me the gravest disquiet — I was given a ticket for my trans-Atlantic passage by air! Not with the Kenyons, but two days later.

And now I must make a confession. A very painful confession, for though my blue jacket was never authenticated, as it were, by a pilot's wings, I did emerge from my service in the Royal Air Force with the rank of Squadron-leader. A good, solid rank, equivalent to Field Officer's rank in the Army. But in spite of that — in spite of my uniform and the dignity of two and a half rings of braid on my cuff — I had never been able to rid myself of a desolating fear of flying across the sea. And now the prospect of traversing in a cloudy sky the whole vast breadth of the Atlantic filled me with an appalling dread: a dread I could not master. — So what, I thought, would Parolles do? And Parolles gave me the answer.

Kenyon was most sympathetic. He perfectly understood my plight when I told him something of my service in the R.A.F. — Those long return flights from bombing missions over Hamburg and Bremen, with an engine or two disabled and the whole fabric of the machine shuddering in its shell-pierced frailty. Then the occasion when we ditched, and for two long days and nights floated, drenched and hungry, in our rubber dinghy. How, defying the doctors, I insisted on returning to duty, and after three more missions, ditched again; and when we were found, I was the only one alive in the dinghy. — After that, I said, I lost my nerve. I could no longer fly across the sea.

With some difficulty Kenyon suppressed his emotion. He got up — I stood too — and shook me warmly by the hand. 'We've certainly got to hand it to you boys in the Royal Air

Force,' he said. 'You did a mighty fine job, and we in the United States, right from the start, recognised and admired what you were doing. Maybe we didn't think too highly of your Army, but from the very beginning we took our hats off to your Air Force. And if you'd rather come over in the *Queen Mary*, I can fix that, and I'll be glad to.'

I accepted his compliments to my service without embarrassment. Though I myself had not earned them, very many of my fellow-officers had — and I too might have had such memories as I pretended had it not been for the unfortunate condition of my semi-circular canals. So dependent are we all on the purely accidental structure of our physical apparatus.

I went with the Kenyons to see them off at London Airport, and returned to my friendly small hotel in Bayswater. I must wait five more days for my passage in the *Queen Mary*, but the manager of the hotel — my old comrade in West Africa and Ceylon — had not thought it strange when I chose to register under an assumed name, and with that protection it seemed unlikely that Olive or Edna would discover where I was. Indeed I welcomed the delay, for it was a long time since I had spent five days in London with my pockets full of money.

But the following morning I woke in a state that bordered on panic. I had been in London since Tuesday night, and this was Saturday. Olive would already be looking for my return, and if I did not come home within the next day or two, she would certainly begin to make enquiries; while Edna, arriving in Llancwmbwlch and finding no one to meet her, no cosy, comfortable bedroom booked for the assuaging of her insatiable hunger — what had Edna done? She had little discretion, very little self-control. In a rage of disappointment she might have been wildly indiscreet, catastrophically intent on revenge. A volcano, intolerably brooding eruption, does not pause to consider where the lava will run.

But what could they do? I tried to calm and comfort myself with the assurance that I had done nothing wrong: I had committed no offence, neither crime nor misdemeanour, nothing they could report to the police. — That was true, but they could, of course, ask the police to make enquiries; and our police are very efficient. Within five days they might well discover my whereabouts, even though I lay lightly hidden under an assumed name — and a worse danger than that was my real name on the *Queen Mary*'s passenger-list! That, if enquiry was made, they would certainly discover, and then at Southampton I would find Olive waiting for me, with her father and her mother to support her — the whole staff of Trumbull, Tranter and Payne in the offing, with the children crying in their arms — and, on the other side of a discreet sergeant of police, Edna in eruption, with her sister Lily and her mother blocking with their bosoms my escape, all the remarkable bosoms of the Buttermere Family Hotel like a balloon-barrage across the gangway. No, Southampton was impossible, and I could not sail in the *Queen Mary*.

But fear — even the whisper of panic-fear — did not unman or disable me. If I did not mean to travel in the *Queen Mary* my name on her passenger-list was a safeguard against discovery, for when the police found it, as they quickly would, they would not bother to search elsewhere, but wait confidently for me in the Customs shed: that I quickly realised. And then I had a stroke of luck.

In my small hotel there were two Italians, man and wife, loud and loquacious. They had lived in England for many years, and now they were going to Genoa to take farewell of two young brothers — his or hers, I did not know — whom the United States had accepted as immigrants. The Italian

couple were flying to Genoa — they were packed and ready
to go — and the two brothers would sail, on Monday morning, in one of the smaller ships of the Livorno–Liguria Line,
the *Torquato Tasso*.

Hearing that, I went immediately to a travel agent and
got a seat in an aeroplane leaving for Nice at half-past one.
I hired a car to take me to London Airport, and for just over
thirty minutes I waited there in an exquisite delicacy of
apprehension. I had no real or positive fear that the police
were looking for me: Olive, I was sure, had as yet no suspicion that I had left her — unless Edna went straight back
to Melbury and blurted out the whole story? Would she do
that — and even if she did, would Olive realise at once its
implications? It was possible, but I thought it unlikely; and
I thought it quite improbable that even if the police were on
my trail, they were near enough to pick me up. But I felt,
I must admit, a little current of excitement: not trepidation,
but a springtime emotion cutting on the outside edge a little
arabesque of fancy on the verge of trepidation.

Then a metallic voice summoned us to the door, and
suddenly I was aware of a calm and perfect comfort, both of
mind and body — except for a slight physical embarrassment and a scarcely perceptible limp due to walking in socks
stuffed full of £5 notes — and the moment we were airborne
I leaned back as blissful as Buddha on his lotos throne.

I have no fear of flying over land, and I enjoyed immensely
the transition from England's jigsaw puzzle of roads and
fields, over the short leap of the Channel, to the orderly pale
rectangles that Norman farmers cultivated; and when, a
little while later, I looked in a trance of delight at the jagged,
tiger-striped palisade of the Alps — Mont Blanc rising in
arrogant splendour under my left arm — I realised in a flood
of emotion my debt to the world I had lived in. Whether it
was a moral debt, or aesthetic, I could not decide; but a debt

it was. I must tell the world what I had learnt of its reality, for I and my ancestors had been sensitive plates exposed to harsh impressions and rabid sunlight — we had been litmus-paper under squalls of acid rain and alkaline summer drenching — we had opened the virgin pages of our diaries to life, and suffered, and survived — and what I owed the world, so far as I could tell it, was the story of the Vanbrughs.

We landed at Nice in a braggart sunshine, and an hour or two later I boarded another aeroplane for Genoa. I spent Sunday in Genoa and a few dollars on completing my arrangements. They made some pretence of difficulty — by 'they' I mean the local representatives of authority, the Genoese chapter of the planetary Establishment — in booking me, at such short notice, the best cabin in the *Torquato Tasso*, but because the Italians constitute a more reasonable chapter of the Establishment than most nations, there was no difficulty that was not soluble in a hard currency; and I could afford a hundred dollars in addition to my fare. My passport was in order, I had my American visa, and we put to sea on the brightest Monday morning I have ever seen.

Of Torquato Tasso — not the ship, but the poet after whom she was named — I knew nothing when I went aboard, but there I soon learnt that in consequence of some indiscretion he spent seven years in prison; and his experience was brought vividly to mind by our voyage. Our ship, otherwise most comfortable, but very old and handicapped by some fault in its engines, took longer to cross the Atlantic than any vessel since square-rigged sailing-ships went out of fashion; and some of my fellow-passengers took umbrage at this tedious crossing. But nothing could have suited me better.

I remembered the vision of my duty — my debt to the world — that I saw so clearly as we flew past the Alps with Mont Blanc under my elbow, and from our first morning out of Genoa I have been a lonely, dedicated man. Every day from dawn to midnight — but for generous meals and an hour or so of walking exercise — I have kept to my cabin, and with an urgency I have never known before I have been writing these pages: this history of my family, so far as it is known.

I had long since sieved and selected those of our family papers that I thought worth preservation, and these I brought with me. I have read them again, and I am utterly convinced that the tale of the Vanbrughs is a tale worth the telling, because, at its apparent end — or, as I choose to think, at its critical centre, at its high noon — here am I, the heir of generations of defeat and disappointment — disappointed and defeated myself — embarking on a new career with all the confidence and eupeptic assurance of old Moses Vanbrugh, first of our line, when, through the servants' door, he forced his way into the hard, bright, aristocratic world of England's 18th century. He from the servants' hall drove a road to the peerage — and so will I! As he did, so in my turn I venture. He into the aristocracy of England, I into the newer aristocracy of Texas. And as he conquered, so shall I. I needed, as he did, a new dimension for my wings. And I shall find it.

I have almost finished my story, and to-morrow we shall see the topless towers of fabulous Manhattan. A few days later, Texas! My heart is on fire.

But England, I have not abandoned you! No more than Clive or Hastings, Raffles or Lugard, Rhodes or Strathcona left you, have I deserted you! No, England, you must not call me renegade. I go but to extend your conquests farther.

I see my destiny, I recognise my genius. I am going into Texas as major-domo on one of the great feudal estates of Texas, and what does major-domo mean but 'mayor of the palace'? Well, were not the kings of France (while there were kings of France) descended from that Pepin who was Mayor of the Palace to some blood-boltered autocrat of the Dark Ages in France? And is my seed not capable of as much? The seed of the Vanbrughs is still potent....

It is indeed, and to that potency I owe, in part, my presence here, in the good ship *Torquato Tasso*, now approaching Nantucket Island, Martha's Vineyard, or Block Island (we are, I am told, a little off course) while far away poor Edna is probably giving it a most grudging acknowledgment in squeamish half-hours after breakfast.

Poor Edna! She was certainly telling the truth when, on the last night we were together, she said she was in the family way. Carelessness you may call it — wilful carelessness — but to me it seems rather an indication of the irresistible life-force of a family pre-destined to greatness.

She and Olive too. A strange co-incidence. But why should they complain? They cannot read the stars, they do not feel the pulse of destiny: that is their only sadness. For when they litter — within the same week, it may be — their pups will be Vanbrughs! True Vanbrughs. And that's reward enough for them.